...they've never read

Yorkshire writer: *Nove*

Ex- Army cat lover: *A unique and intuitive insight into human behaviour from the feline point of view.*

School teacher: *Reminded me very much of Bridget Jones' diary!*

Teenager and cat lover: *Made me laugh out loud more than once…gave me a whole new perspective on my furry friends. Got me thinking like a cat.*

Housewife and cat owner: *A dire warning to all prospective Chow (dog) owners.*

Court reporter and dog owner: *Not everyone's family is a Mom, Dad and block kids!*

Company director, cat and dog owner: *Absorbing revelations from a cat who refuses to go quietly.*

West Highland terrier (dog) owner: *A book you can dip into and enjoy!*

Former home economist: *Will also appeal to Mrs Pumphrey and 'Tricky Woo' types!*

First published in Great Britain
in 2007 by Mspec.co.uk

This edition published in 2007 by
Mspec.co.uk
P.O. Box 936
Camberley GU15 9EG
United Kingdom

A CIP catalogue record for this book
is available from the British Library.

ISBN 978-0-9556286-0-3

Designed by Mspec.co.uk
Printed and bound in Great Britain
by RapSpiderweb

by A. S. Cat

LIFE

IN THE

CAT'S LANE

The 1st of the Pets Diaries

Mspec.co.uk

A. S. Cat

Certified authentic

DH Cmber

30 January 2008

Acknowledgements

A.S. Cat would like to thank the following, including several dogs, for their contributions – direct and indirect:

- His editor's former "pets": black cat Piewacket and American short-haired silver tabby Smokey (a whiner) as well as golden labrador Lord Geordie (Sam) and Chow Chow Oso ("Bear" in Spanish)

- Late pussycat Whisky, whose "owner" is a champion mouser, as well as Whisky's former companions, the late golden retriever Mayo (life-long sex goddess) and labradors Bonnie and Tess

- Half-Tibetan spaniel Smudge

- Lurchers FloJo and Twiggy, golden retrievers Sam and Fella, Cairn terrier Elsa, lurcher Mumbai plus a host of other Southerners including Callie and Meg

- Friends of the North: black labrador Daisy, Westie Rowan and whippet Millie

Thanks too to some of THEM (the diarist's human acquaintances) for ongoing tittle tattle about their "pets" as well as to D. H. Carter, who served as Cat's editor and secured the copyright to this work on his behalf.

A.S. Cat

About the Diarist

A. S. Cat was born in Newcastle upon Tyne in the North of England in the mid-1980's. He was later educated on the back streets of a suburb called Forest Hall. A self-made moggy, he is believed to have spent his early childhood in the home of a retired Professor of Shakespearean Literature. After the latter's death Cat repaired to one of the city's animal shelters for a brief respite. A short time later he took up residence with a company director who moved to the South of England.

An exceptional memory along with speech-recognition technology and purr-activated word processing facilitated by his human editor, D.H. Carter, has enabled Cat to translate his life experience and wisdom -- imparted by 100 different vocalisation sounds (e.g. meows) – into diary form, for "the educational benefit of humankind" as he would put it. With the release of *Life in the Cat's Lane*, A.S. Cat is becoming widely recognised as a Diarist Extraordinaire within the Animal Kingdom.

He is also noted for expressing unpopular views, one of them being that "the finest achievement any human can attain is engendering the respect of a cat." Which, he has suggested on numerous occasions, is a "nigh impossible task for any man or woman and out of the question for dogs."

Who's Who in the Diary
(in alphabetical order, to reduce reader confusion)

Arthur: South African businessman speared by a dog bone

Bobbin' Robin: pesky wingsnapper who teases Cat

Cowboy Bebop: rapacious corgi who moves next door to Cat

Dog/It: squirrelous Chow invader of Cat's household

Drusilla Fence: ex bag lady neighbour from Hackney

Edward and Raymond: gay owners of *Poochini's Paradise*

Fat Fiona: weighty policewoman and criminologist friend of Cat's alleged owner

Gazelda: eccentric Chow breeder of Cat's dog nemesis

Lady Tattersley: dispenser of drugs for Fireworks Dementia

Lying Hound: chimney-smoking American ex-boyfriend of Cat's alleged owner

Mad Larissa: fallen-on-hard-times widow and neighbour

Mangle and Wurzel: manic Westies at the end of Cat's road

Marigold Scallionrapper: mother of Cat's owner's godson Rupert who was appointed as Dog's godfather

Petronella: clawless silver tabby object of Cat's affections

Precocious Brat: potential replacement for ex-Lying Hound

Miss Dawgsbody: founder of *Pooch Perfect* dog training school who subjected Cat's alleged owner to public humiliation

Saffron: one of Cat's alleged owner's more "useful" friends

She/Her: Cat's all-too-human, adoring and hapless minder and "alleged owner"

Sheldon Prattlebury: camp friend of Cat's alleged owner

Smudge: half-Tibetan spaniel and Dog's first boyfriend

Stinking Squirrel: the tree rat who brought Cat down

Zara: four-times married poodle-prissy friend of Hers

CONTENTS

GLOSSARY FOR HUMAN READERS

Cat word	Human translation
Animal + pat (+ bat)	Lowest form of indicated beast, e.g. cowpat, chowpat, dogbat etc.
Anglophiliacal	Anglophile crossed with maniac
Bugstration	Acute frustration
Catalytical	Profoundly astute and analytical, commonly associated with feline species
Catterwailing	Wallowing in self pity (as humans do)
Claw duggery	Feline practice for controlling humans
Crowspeke	Gibberish, nonsense, illogic etc
Exfurriation	The casting off of fur (as in case of dogs)
Grrr-ow	Feline expression of displeasure
Monotribe	Bitter, abusive outpouring of human speech
Pawstompers	Illbred dogs in veterinary reception areas
PRRR Maximus	Feline expression of supreme satisfaction
Scumbugs	Utterance of profound distaste or irritation
Smarm queen	A conniving, untrustworthy human female
Snifter	An especially insulting term for a dog
Squirrelous	Meaning deviant, criminal, corrupt and/or covertly unethical as associated with humans and to a lesser extent, dogs
Wagger	Animal who bows and scrapes to humans, primarily applying to dogs
Waglessness	A canine expression of disgust with humans, rarely observed in the species except for the Chow breed

Reality in the Extreme

Let me get *one* thing straight! This story is not simply "awfully true." It's more than that – it's *A Superior Cat's* account of reality in the extreme. I know it is – I've lived it, been there, seen Her (my alleged owner) in action daily for more years than I care to remember. Be under no illusion – real events, real people and real cats and dogs are chronicled in this diary e.g. there *was* a *Rat News*, She *did* dress up as me for Halloween, Dog (my nemesis) *was* called "a wicked little bitch" at Obedience School. Of course, my human editor (D.H. Carter) insisted on exaggerating some events out of all proportion to their mundane reality because humans love embroidering truth!

Names and personalities of men and women are intentionally muddied to disguise the guilty, and avoid litigation. But many animals are authentic; even humans would be hard pressed to put a cat on the stand -- no reputable judge would hear of it!

I am not afraid to give you the indisputable facts of my life as A Superior Cat. After all, it is only because of me that this remarkable account exists; it's not because of the publishers, or the printers, or retailers or distributors. But me, and all my talents and experience, that this catalytical view of human events has come to light.

Make no mistake, I'm no fancy pants puss. No king of the jungle or prince of the back garden boasting of "papers" or five-generation pedigrees. Self-respecting, yes, but thankfully not posh although of similar likeness to one celebrity puss on a cat food tin. You know the one – black with white nose and paws who looks like he's wearing a dinner suit?

Although I as A Superior Cat am not ordinary, the name I was given is horribly common – Sooty, after some mucky has-been English puppet who fascinated Her as a child although said puppet was basically nothing more than a *faux* fur teddy bear head on a glove from a Blackpool junk shop. Frankly, I would have preferred a name with more panache, something double barrelled or mean sounding to strike fear into the hearts of vermin. Growl Tiger perhaps, Mephistopheles or Lucifer. But oh no, an Anglophiliacal human had to name me after a hyperactive toy who hung out with a moronic-looking Spaniel. As if that weren't bad enough, She – my alleged owner that is – and Her lot call me all sorts of other absurd things like Soot Soot, Sootster, pussykins and similar rubbish. The ignominy of more than one stupid name!

Then again, my alleged owner is only human. I say "alleged" because She doesn't actually own me. As even the least self-aware of us knows, no one *owns* a cat.

A cat of a certain age I may be (119 if I were a DOG, by illogical human calculation) but we cats are always learning new tricks. We don't get old, like dogs or humans. We are quite simply cats to the end. And just because some trumped up wolf offshoot darkens my door, don't think I shall go quietly into the good night. For as A Superior Cat I go when and where I please and I shall always, and I mean always, have the last word on whatever topic of discussion is on the table: human, dog or otherwise.

On the subject of humans, I have spent well over a decade living with Her – a former "highflying" corporate executive now consigned to the trenches of self-employment. Yes, SHE has a name. But I refuse to use it. Certainly not, not after suffering through all her Bad Hair Days lasting for years, cheap and cheerful cat food, six house removals and workaholic ways. Never mind the wretched boyfriends who'd have strung me up by the tail.

When all's said and done, She's been rather a trial. Is it her father's American heritage, I ask myself? An upbringing that condones being impolitely direct and outspoken? None of the subtlety of an English mother has imprinted *Her* brain! Or could it be Her penchant to act before thinking? Even some of Her friends say she's a "nutter" and "eccentric" amid vigorous head shaking.

Ah well, She does *try* to relate to me – albeit unsuc-cessfully most of the time. Which means I've had to invest years studying her language and convoluted ways since She's genetically incapable of interpreting mine. From the moment She "rescued me" at aged two from an animal shelter, I saw the training task ahead would be monumental, a life's work to be sure. So, after ages of brushing my whiskers against the limbs of Her humanity, I decided – it was time for A.S. Cat to go public with his diary to expose how **LOW** a human could stoop!

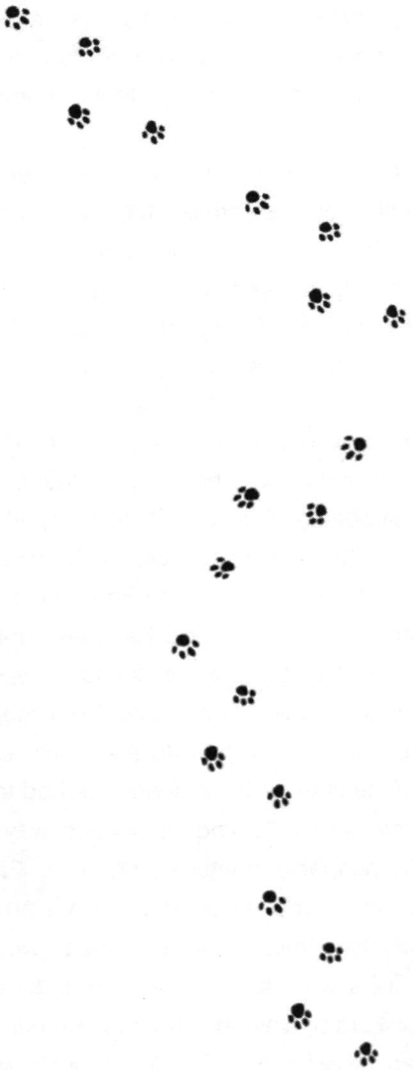

May: A Stinking Fish of a Month

Wednesday, 28th May: *False sense of security?*

High noon in my back garden: I am purring and licking my paws because all seems well in my world as I lie like a lounge lizard on the toasty stones of my shrub-bordered terrace soaking up late spring sun. At least I *think* all's well…

Weather: warming up nicely; more opportunity to luxuriate on the grass during the day with sultry nights out on mini prowls in search of the new posh puss down our road

Hunting prospects: up on previous month – with growing streams of field mice plus chances to catch the Stinking Squirrel who's trying to muscle in on the lower ground of my split-level garden, to set up house in one of the conifers

Food: anticipate higher-than-normal amounts of tuna chunks in brine due to "owner's" likely failure to grocery shop (latter sabotaged by Her workaholic ways)

Accommodation: acceptable despite being downsized from spacious detached dwelling into flat conversion in older house with 24/7 access to Her bed, office and lounge, not to mention all other areas of her living space although Her use of *my* terrace and garden could be more restricted

Dogwatch: neighbourhood pooch population dwindling as a result of the rise in dual-career households and people's cat preferences despite distant rumblings of a renewed canine influx

5

Entertainment: promising -- the 70-year-old tortoise Sid, who lives three houses down from mine, is scheduled to come out of hibernation to hump concrete "garden ornament" Cynthia (bought by Sid's owners as a companion for him); otherwise Cynthia languishes unfulfilled on our neighbour's terrace; alternatively, I could chase Bobbin' Robin who's forever trying to taunt me with a worm dripping out of his mouth. Of course there is one issue which is *not* moving forward and that is…

Her training: which is at a standstill because I'd rather spend my valuable time stalking the Stinking Squirrel.

But overall, I have to say – prospects seem excellent for a lazy and idle summer although there *are* signs of secret-squirrel activity; Her behaviours of the past few weeks have been slightly more bizarre than normal.

Take the case of ***Her unexplained trip***. Last month midweek She drove to the south coast for three days. Odd. It wasn't business – She went wearing a track suit and carrying a small duffel bag packed with one pair of jeans, two T-shirts, a pair of flat black shoes (according to Her at the time of purchase, "a steal") plus knickers falling to bits. *Definitely* no men involved.

Neither did She take her "horribly expensive" trainers for walking. More to the point, she did not advise me of her itinerary before leaving and said nothing about the trip afterwards. The only clues as to Her whereabouts came via snatches of a telephone conversation She had with her best friend Fat Fiona the morning after her return when I was eating breakfast. *Note:* Fat Fiona is Her name for a

15-stone policewoman whom I would say resembles a Cheshire cat -- she's forever smiling.

In between tuna chunks, I heard Her mention "one ageing boxer, six scraggy cats, two shrieking parrots and 17 woolly bears running around the garden," all of which made me wonder – had She gone to some kind of zoo? Aside from the unexplained trip, there's also the matter of the **_unidentified carry bags_**.

A few weeks after Her trip to the coast, She arrived home from shopping with a plastic carry bag bulging with something squeakable. She put the bag down on the kitchen floor and inadvertently stepped on it when turning round to open a cupboard under the sink. Out came a short, sharp squeak. Which struck me as more than discordant – it was *not* my birthday and she never starts Christmas shopping, even for me, until late November at the earliest. Plus, although I was sitting right beside the bag when it squeaked, She made no comment. Nor even glanced in my direction. In fact, I'd say She consciously avoided looking at me. And, instead of unpacking the bag, She stuffed it full to bursting into the cupboard. Hmm!

Oh yes, and that's not the only carry bag which has come into my house and been squirreled away without explanation. I've noted at least two others: one stashed in Her bedroom closet and another put into the storage cupboard in Her office. She didn't mention anything about either of them, which is highly suspicious in light of Her propensity to chatter non-stop to me after any shopping spree, even midnight ones to Tesco to pick up her favourite chocolate ice cream.

In addition to the mysterious carry bags, I have had to endure **behind-closed-doors chats**, referring to lengthy ones She's been having on the telephone behind closed doors. Closed to me anyway. These are also untoward given during the past 15 years of our association, I have been privy – sometimes against my will -- to every conversation, discussion, debate, argument, castigation or enraged outburst She's ever had in my house or over the phone.

Now, every time the phone rings and it's someone She calls Gazelda, She says, "Ah, can you hold on a minute, I just have to check where everyone is…" With that she looks around to see "where everyone is" (albeit normally She refers to me as "you-know-who" when plotting behind my back) and if I'm in the room, Her jolly-hockey-sticks voice says something like, "Pussycat, there you are (when She knows full well where I am!), how about going out for a wee." Which isn't a question.

More recently, my alleged owner arrived home from an alleged "business trip" carrying not her usual briefcase (a tatty black vinyl job with a diagonal red stripe across its front made in Taiwan and costing £15, she never fails to point out) but a large item resembling a **flattened metal suitcase** of criss-crossing wires. I could tell it was heavy -- She had to use both hands to lug it into the house where she took it immediately into her office.

I followed and when I sat down and looked up at Her, was totally ignored – She said nothing. Which is most out of character as she usually answers all my unspoken questions immediately -- most especially the one, "What have you bought *this* time?" She's often so excited about her latest bargain that if I'm sitting in the driveway, even before she's out of the car, I'll hear Her spluttering something like, "Hey there, Soots, got a great deal on shoes today – half price and ALL leather!"

More to the point, the day after the mysterious metal suitcase arrived, She **rearranged Her office** by removing four stacks of cardboard boxes which had towered in one corner for more than a year, ever since the Lying Hound ex-boyfriend disappeared. Without any explanation She deposited the boxes in the outdoor cupboard at the entrance to our house where She normally stores my cat carrier (porta-kennel), leaving a huge empty space. Then She laid the criss-crossing wire contraption down on one side and left it, for reasons I cannot fathom. It's still there, too!

Grrr-ow! – What is She up to?

Late evening, curled up on Her bed thinking whilst She snores: Tonight's meal was woefully inadequate. It was left-over smoked salmon served to me yet again despite the fact I never do more than nose the slimy strips around the inside of my bowl. Hate the smell. Worse - hate Her assumption that because I'm a cat, I'll accept the greaseball fish as a tasty treat. When will She learn – I am *not* like everyone else!

That aside, a funny thing happened before bedtime. She came into the lounge wearing what her mother describes as Her "holier-than-thou," navy-blue, silk-with-grey-elephants pyjamas, hoisted me up off the carpet and set me back down on the sofa for a cuddle. Although She tried to encourage me to face her, I took up my preferred laptop position of *Egyptian Sphinx in repose*, with my back to Her front. This allows me to grip her lower thighs with my front claws should discipline be required whilst lowering the probability of any sneezing created by allergic reactions to Her cinnamon-and-clove perfume.

Per usual She broke the silence, by lacing pigeon coo with maple syrup, in a manner of speaking: "Good Pussycat, you really are the best, you know." After which I had to endure nose nuzzling directed at the top of my head while two of Her fingers rubbed the underside of my chin. Not altogether objectionable. However -- and this is important – pigeon cooing is a reliable Sleaze Indicator. Any attempt by Her to impersonate a female trying soft and sexy on a mate doesn't ring true; She would rather kick a white crap dispenser out of a tree than preen the male ego in it, even if the opposite-sex pigeon were capable of foraging for nesting material.

I chose to escape and dug my front claws into her knees to allow a speedy exit, which 100% of the time precipitates a particularly high-pitched bird shriek. This occasion proved no exception. "Puss, why MUST you do that?" I heard frantic thigh rubbing as I scurried to safety underneath our "very valuable" antique Welsh dresser. She was suitably miffed. "Okay, Soots, be like that – but you'll miss me when I'm gone!"

Typical human -- face-saving to the end.

Under the dresser I had time to ponder, tail flat on the floor: Why is She taking such pains to state the obvious?

Cats *know* we're No 1. What's behind Her sudden declaration of undying loyalty? What's really going on here? Do I need to re-think my summer plans and schedule more training after all? Rats if I do!

Thursday, 29th May: *A Day of Infamy*

Much too early in the morning*:* Strange goings on. They commenced in the bedroom when Her alarm clock shattered my deep sleep and squirrel-chasing dream at the crack of dawn. As soon as the odious buzzer went off, She had the audacity to fling her double-size duvet over my head while catapulting out of bed without nary a backward glance to see if cat still breathing. Even after thumping the clock into silence, She didn't return to bed. Nor did She utter one word of greeting or apology.

Grossly out of character. She always resets her clock to ring a second time before getting up and never – I mean *never ever* -- starts any day without speaking to me first. But this morning, as observed from my peephole vantage point under the duvet, She simply grabbed her white terrycloth bathrobe (bought for a 30% discount in a New Year's sale) off the hook of the bedroom door and stumbled out of the room towards her office across the hallway. After that I heard the office door shut. Extremely abnormal – She hardly ever closes that door and certainly not when yours truly is outside the office. "Bad feng shui, Soot," She'd say. "We simply must keep the energy flowing throughout our living space at all times."

I went to investigate but finding the office door shut, had to take up an observation post in my slightly listing sheepskin hammock suspended from the radiator opposite. ("I promise I'll sew up that corner tomorrow, Puss" has been Her party line for the past three months. The same goes for our doorbell which has been "under repair" for several years.)

I couldn't see into Her office obviously but it sounded impossibly as though a fencing match was taking place. Heard lots of metal bashing interspersed with heavy breathing. Finally the penny dropped – She must be wrestling with that wire suitcase thing. Suddenly, my ears were severely pricked by Her nasal twanging, "Oh shit, why the bloody hell can't anyone write bloody decent instructions anyway!" (She has nil understanding of anything remotely mechanical, technical or constructional.)

After Her cat-spitting expletives, I heard more metal bashing and floor thumping and realised Her bad behaviour was taxing my own energy flow. I went back to sleep in my hammock until the whistling of Her electric tea kettle, fridge door banging and irritating sing-songy "time for brekkies" call ruined my fantastical mouse chase.

"Sooty Soot, time to get uhhh-uppp. C'mon Puss, I've got a special treat for you." She was using her molasses tone of voice whose only saving grace was the rattling of dry biscuits against my porcelain bowl in the background. Despite the promised "special treat," my training programme demanded a swift exit into the lounge to hide under our sofa, especially as Her office door was shut. *Never do "brekkies" on request* (or any other meal for that matter) is one of Ten Cat Commandments for Human Socialisation.

In response to Her summons, I'd planned to stay hidden for at least five minutes to make a point despite experience that most of cat's points are missed. But I didn't get the chance to make a point. After less than 30 seconds into the training exercise, She got downright shirty with me. "Okay, Pussycat, have it your own way, don't come eat your breakfast, but don't meow about it when it's gone all dry and crusty. I've no time to muck about with you today." Patience is *not* one of Her virtues. Grrr-ow. My tail swishes like a windshield wiper at the thought of how far Her obedience level has fallen.

Inspite of Her remonstrations I stayed put under the sofa until – and this is positively embarrassing to report – with two more minutes to go, I heard the front door shut and her car start up and pull out of the driveway. Which made me spitting mad. It was a flagrant disregard of my training regimen. However, curiosity about the "special treat" did distract. Whereupon, I crawled out and stalked into the kitchen to view the promised culinary delight waiting in my blue-and-white bowl. (My bowl is one of the surviving pieces of an old willow-pattern dinnerware set She claims is "too good for the charity shops.")

As I meandered towards my destination, my nose picked up the slippery smell of – yes it was – boiled ham (smoked utterly unacceptable) and ah, purr purr, medium cheddar cheese. My whiskers began twitching even before my eyes feasted on the dry biscuit laden with small chunks of my favourite pink and yellow goodies. It was a bona fide special treat after all and I did Her the favour of eating it.

But now that I'm lying back on the duvet of Her unmade bed, I have to wonder -- WHY did She give it to me? WHAT is so special about today? WHY was She fencing with the metal suitcase? In thinking more about it all, I am not amused – indeed, my tail is swishing at 180 degrees. She is up to something and it has an oily-fishy smell.

Afternoon, sun above my head in the back garden: I am now reclining like a Sphinx on the back terrace, eyes slitty, to catch up on my sleep. Still no sign of Her although she's been gone for hours. Only entertainment prospect at present is Bobbin' Robin, who's just parachuted out of the holly bush. But I've no interest in expunging the red-breasted terrace hopper. Am far too preoccupied analysing the significance of:

1. Her unexplained trip to the south coast mid week
2. Her unqualified references to an aged boxer, scraggly cats, shrieking parrots and woolly bears (Since when are bears woolly? !!!)
3. Storage of unidentified, squeaking carry bags
4. Her hush hush conversations with strangers
5. Her deposit of a metal suitcase object in the office
6. Worse, Her barring of cat's entry into the office
7. Dispensation of special treats for no apparent reason
8. The dramatic rise in Her Disobedience Level.

Grrr-ow! These implications have occurred to me:

- Cat is currently losing grip = worst-case scenario = lowest probable possibility.
- She is losing grip of self = nothing new = so what?

- "Something is ruddy rotting in the state of Bismarck" = Her words = more than likely.

Afternoon, sun lower in sky: I am surfacing from a deep-level snooze on the terrace at the dull roar of Her car in the drive spilling out the cackle cackle of only two familiar voices, Hers and Fat Fiona's. Hmmm -- why is one of my right whiskers twitching and my back fur standing on end? Why is a smell of stinking oily fish assaulting my nostrils, figuratively speaking?

I am now back arching on all fours contemplating scaling the red brick wall built between our back terrace and front driveway. Doing so would be enlightening except that it will also put me in Her sight lines and I absolutely do not wish to appear interested in human affairs. I will listen in from this side of the wall.

Weird. Fat Fiona has just asked, "Are all of them like stunted red lions?" Are all of WHO like "stunted red lions" for goodness sake? Bugstration! – I wish I could see what's going on outside my house!

Evening, sun down behind hellhole of house abandoned by A.S. Cat who is now crouching under the conifer in his back garden: Oh, women, women, smiling damned females! Deliverers of the biggest, baddest stinking fish imaginable! And I am categorically *not* referring to the arrival of some smelly-orange-tabby-cat charity case although the "stunted lion" mention put me off the scent of the real plague descending upon my house.

With Fat Fiona's abstruse question added to all the observed secret-squirrel data, I initially thought She had indulged in some misdirected but well intentioned goody-two-shoes work. Like bringing home an abused rescue puss which I was to take charge of when my too-good-for-the-charity-shops, willow-pattern food bowl is already over-flowing with training responsibilities! Except the predicted flea-bag *cat* didn't materialise. Her rabid alarm clock heralded a more shocking Day of Infamy.

After crawling back through my cat flap into the kitchen, I began walking sedately – as only cats do -- down the hallway towards the front door. That's when I picked up snatches of sleaseball cooings (Hers) and indecipherable mutterings (Fat Fiona's) about "a little baggage" while the two She-devils tried to stifle atrocious bouts of giggling amid Her shushings.

Thereafter, a heavy stillness descended, broken only by a key turning ever so slowly in the door lock followed by a soft spray of hoarse whispers and – here I froze with tail in full extension motionless when I heard the next – an unmistakeable sniff, sniff, sniffing and muted but insistent scratch, scratch, scratching behind the door. By then I was crouching down and leaning forward in mid-stride, spine and tail parallel to the floor, ears pricked into miniscule tents. Not to mention, my eyes were opening wide into owl's eyes while my nose vibrated in futile attempts to identify the foreign odour seeping under the door like a slowly advancing army of ghostly mice stealing into all corners of the house in deathly silence.

All at once I knew with dreadful certainty – there was no feline beggar behind the door, meowing and tail twitching for room and board. I looked up and saw the door open a crack. There was non-human panting and in its wake -- Her bird shriek, "Fiona, no, no, DON'T let her in yet! You-know-who may ..." sputtered into nothingness as the awful truth burst forth into my house. Bang, crash, wallop! – the front door smashed against the wall of the hallway as a racing demon **DOG!!!!!** (obviously, the aforementioned "stunted red lion" !) with oh-so-big paws did not wait to be introduced.

A tiny monster smaller than me rushed in as though It owned cat's place! No polite glance of acknowledgement was forthcoming. The creature simply squashed its pug nose into the carpet and started hoovering while an absurd curled-up tail wiggled high on Its back like a feather duster.

"Out, damned spot," I yowled. After which millennia of instinct curved my spine into a perfect semi circle for a pre-emptive strike. My claws metamorphosed into two switchblades to cut the ugly fiend down. Followed by a carefully orchestrated GRRR-OW MAXIMUS and spitting to get the demon's attention. Which succeeded – the Red Scourge looked up and stopped dead in Its stubby-little-paw tracks before turning tail and scampering back outside into the supremely squirrelous alleged owner's arms. After which the equally squirrelous owner's friend spluttered fawning "sorrys" and bulldozed her way inside to pull the door shut and reconstruct a barrier between one severely compromised cat and not two but three She-devils.

I stood like stone, my grrr-ow maximus downgrading to a grrrow-on-your-bike growling, with every bit of fur and whisker on end as I waited, poised for a second assault. Pointless questions were spewing forth: WHAT is a DOG doing in cat's house? WHOSE dog is it? Is She only taking care of some squirrelous canine temporarily? Is A Superior Cat over-reacting?

Before I could ask any more, She reopened the door and stepped back into the hallway with the wretched "little baggage" cradled tightly in her arms. A bear-like paw spilled over her forearm and a foul purple-black tongue was poking out of a twitching furry mouth. "Good girl, that's a good puppy," She was smarm cooing and methodically stroking and cuddling the beast. Her besotted smile shattered my vain hope that the creature wasn't here to stay. Fat Fiona stood shushed into obedient silence.

She then tried to calm me down. "Sooty, Soot, it's all right, Pussycat. It's only our new puppy." ONLY OUR NEW PUPPY??? – four little words describing ONLY the worst disaster of my life! I'd have spat in her face had I thought Her capable of comprehending the act's significance. Instead, I held my ground in silence, tail upright and twitching furiously, hoping I had red-glinting eyes communicating utter disdain. At least the furball had the grace to be quiet.

She chattered on. I found it hard to listen. My whole life was passing before my eyes – years of dedicated training, ceaseless efforts to correct Her aberrant behaviour, capped by unfulfilled dreams of total obedience while She droned on … "and doggy's only three months old" and on until I turned away, head held high, and walked slowly but resolutely down the hallway without looking back, not even after I'd slithered through the cat flap with a scornful purr, *Hell hath no fury like a cat scorned!*

Friday, 30th May: *Questions, questions*
Dull grey sunless morning in back garden: I am still intact as A Superior Cat. The clatter of the back door being shoved open has thankfully broken up my nightmare of being ground down into catburger by a rampaging, King-Kong-size Bull Dog. Am extremely relieved – as I see no great white canine jaws anywhere. Just green grass and low-hanging branches of the conifer I'm lying under. Except now I remember – yesterday was a Day of Infamy. My dream reflects harsh reality.

Grrr-ow! I can hear Her issuing a horribly irritating, early-morning, bright-and-breezy "Pussycat, where ARE yooou? Brekkies!" summons for my first feed of the day as though nothing's changed when everything's different. **Question:** will there be more special treats in my willow-pattern food bowl in light of Her shock-horror betrayal? My head droops at the growing weight of other questions:

- How long will the demon dog actually live?
  Longer than me?
- Where does It think it's going to sleep?
- What does It eat?
- Does She seriously expect me to welcome It?
- Which part of my home will It be allowed in?
- Is It house trained?
- What breed of pooch pisser is It anyway?

19

After breakfast: Prrr! There's a speck of light at the end of the rat tunnel of my life although I'm back in the damp grass under the conifer instead of enjoying my usual morning nap in Her office. Speck of light = tummy full from second round of special treats in less than 24 hours. Treats = tuna chunks *in spring water* plus boiled ham plus even larger squares of medium cheddar as well as an unsolicited present of one shiny new metal food bowl with a black rubber non-slip bottom and the letters C-A-T embossed on one side.

Alleged owner is clearly consumed by King-Kong-size guilt pangs following cat's totally justified refusal "to come say hello to doggy." Prrr, prrr, prrr – I can now see potential benefits in the canine disaster i.e. new training opportunities could emerge. And I have learned that:

1. The pigmy lion will be shut in a crate in Her office until It's house trained. (Metal suitcase mystery solved)
2. My breakfast routine will be altered i.e. She will lift "the premier pet" up onto the kitchen counter so that A. S. Cat can "eat in peace."

Which nevertheless means post-breakfast naps on Her office ottoman will be indefinitely suspended due to No 1.

Afternoon, crouching on back terrace: Had to endure compulsory first audience with It following an unpleasant interception by Her during my intended return to the hammock earlier. "Sooty, perfect timing, Pussycat," She'd smarm queened at me whilst swooping down on my person when only three-quarters of A.S. Cat's body was through the cat flap. She looked all smiley, smiley, let's

20

party, unceremoniously picked me up and slung me over her shoulder to carry me down the hallway to her office. Where She set me down in front of a huge metal crate rising up from the floor like a massive transparent box of criss-crossing wires.

"Here we are, Mr Soots." She cheerily dropped into what could only be described as chimpanzee stance with her back to the crate. Thereupon commenced furious head patting of me, undoubtedly to relieve Her own escalating anxiety at the impending confrontation.

"Grrr-ow! Prrr! Grrr-ow!" I protested, refusing to look at her, before I half shut my eyes as cats do when bored or contemplating sleep. Through slitty lids, I saw Her transform from chimp into yogi. She pushed her nose into mine. The palms of both hands rested on her knees. I rose up in front of Her like a 600 B.C. cat god – silent, revered, unwilling to suffer fools gladly.

"Puss Puss," She was begging for my attention. I remained god-like.

"Soot, look at me." More begging. Nary a purr from me.

"C'mon Puss, open your eyes."

I made no move to comply after which She proceeded with formal introductions anyway. Boring the paws off me with a litany of I'm-so-clever facts about Dog's Chinese origins, Its "superior" Chow breeding and Dog's "incredibly original" name in the opinion of Fat Fiona. "Tamba Ching but Tamba to you, Puss", She magnanimously offered. I yawned back.

Eventually, the American mosquito buzzing in my ears stopped. She got up off the floor with a sigh bordering on

21

bugstration. "Right, Sooty, I'm done. You're on your own." And flounced off towards the kitchen.

With Her out of the way, I slowly opened my eyes, remaining god-like of course with tail moulded to my legs and nose and whiskers stock still. And there It was -- the pigmy lion and "little baggage" was sitting behind the crate door, remarkably quiet, with tiny almond-shaped black eyes, pointy ears and impossible-to-read nose twitches. In no time it tried to approach me with a mouse-like *Squeak*! I sat like stone – approach rejected.

Squeak! Squeak! It persisted, putting a tiny podgy paw up onto the crate wall. I pretended to look through It while trying to get a fix on its scent.

Surprisingly, It didn't smell of anything much. Often dogs smell foul – like mouldy blankets, especially when wet. Their personal hygiene leaves much to be desired. They itch and scratch relentlessly. Unlike us they don't wash very often. Expect others to groom them. Disgusting creatures really. But It didn't smell.

Of course, being a dog, It began to behave appallingly: started rushing back and forth along the front of its cage like a tiger during feeding time at the zoo, albeit squeaking like an agitated mouse. That's when I saw its ugly purple-black tongue again. Typical -- She goes out, gets a breeding dog and it's defective!

Moments later It stopped in front of me, pushed its nose against the wire as if daring to sniff me. When I failed to react, it started yelping and clawing at the cage, producing an abominable performance. The peripatetic creature was frantically attempting to communicate –

failing to interpret the message in my stance; namely, *hell will freeze before I grace YOU with a meow.*

The longer I sat there silent and unflinching, the more It squirmed and misbehaved. She obviously heard all the commotion, came rushing back into the office.

"It's all right, little pupsydoodle." She cooed, crouching down by the crate's door while starting to finger stroke It through the mesh. "It's just our pussycat come to say hello." She was comforting It with no concern for me.

I grrr-owed, "More like, goodbye and good riddance, furry cretin." She interrupted, "Soot, Soot, stop growling – you're scaring doggy." Her conciliatory tone walked a tightrope between wanting to silence me totally and not wanting to build up my resentment of "pupsydoodle." Ordinarily, I'd have been irritated by such transparency but the Chow's reaction was in fact a puzzlement. For all Its running around and carrying on, it did not in truth look or smell the least bit scared, which surprised me given It had just lost its mother.

The dog appears slightly disgruntled. Reminds me of Her teddy bear Petula, who grimaces like a permanent crosspatch with a crease running down the middle of its forehead. No trace of fear, anger or sadness in the puppy's sharp little eyes, however. No respect either.

My tail jerked into a full swish. The meaning of Dog's expression struck me with the force of a killer whale: the "little baggage" was quite simply and most horribly CURIOUS, which on reflection is truly, madly, deeply, distressingly disturbing in something so young, let alone a dog! Who's ever heard of a curious dog? Anyone with

23

half a brain knows – a dog's curiosity starts and stops with its stomach. Curious cats – well, yes, of course, even humans appreciate cats are curious, possessed of high intellect, powerful sensitivities and superior natures. But curious dogs? – No, never, by definition impossible.

Curiosity indicates a desire to investigate and learn. What dog ever wanted to do that? Most of them have only one thing on their minds – bow wowing and scraping at the shoes of humans to feed their tummies! Trust Her to complicate my final years with a flipping curious dog!

One thing's sure – I won't be sleeping with Her tonight!

Saturday, 31st May: *Villainy, thy name is HUMAN!*
Early morning, after damp cold wet night outside: I am back on the terrace planning my next move after leaving the house in a huff last night, despite persistent rain and cold damp. Was determined not to sleep on Her bed, or in my falling-apart sheepskin hammock for that matter. Even resisted Her bordering on frantic *Sooty-where-ARE-you-time-for-beddy-bye* summons. I chose instead to visit Mad Larissa, Her name for the downtrodden widow of a former English army colonel, who lives two houses down from ours, next to Sid the tortoise.

"We lived in IND-JA in the days of the Raj, you know" Mad Larissa proclaims almost every time I enter through the cat flap of her house. The cat flap is the only evidence of her "dearly departed beloved pussycat" Trotsi, a feline who was killed by an overdose of rat poison. The cat is "dreadfully missed" Mad Larissa tells me even though I

24

know it was only a main chancer looking for rich pickings in suburbia after hopping a train out of London.

One day after Trotsi's demise, Mad Larissa saw me sitting at the bottom of her garden and invited me in for tea and biscuits consisting of warm milk and fish-flavoured cat crunchies on the side. Since then she has been delighted for me (whom she calls "Catterpuss") to come and go as I please. Even allows me to sleep on the top of her kitchen cupboard near the boiler when it suits.

Nowadays Mad Larissa forgets my tea and biscuits but she also neglects to feed herself, according to Her, so I don't take the oversight personally. At least the old woman offers me another home when needed, like last night when I was desperate to get out of the rain after leaving Her bed.

Note: Up to now I've been sleeping with Her ever since the ghastly Lying Hound boyfriend stalked off. He was another in a long line of male misfits She's brought home over the years. This one always rushed about like a headless rabbit while crowing into a mobile phone between drags on endless, foul-smelling cigarettes.

It was patently obvious he was a wastrel. I couldn't get out of the house fast enough whenever he appeared. If I did hang around, I had to endure him pretending to like me. "Love me, love my cat," She'd purred to him soon after they'd met when she sensed what I'd known instantly – he detested cats.

From there on the Hound made concerted albeit totally disingenuous efforts to "love" me. An unmitigated fraud he was! Which meant regularly trying to scratch me behind the ears, but only when She was around to see it.

My favourite trick was to routinely leap onto one of his shoulders from the back of the settee while She was sitting beside him. Forcing him to be nice to me as I was thoroughly enjoying digging my claws into his hairy skin at the exact moment She would be saying, "Oh, Darling, look how Puss Puss loves you!"

He would wince as I hit his shoulder. But having to accept *my* rules of engagement whenever we were in Her presence, he made no attempt to brush me aside. He soon learned, being human and the beneficiary of my regular tutelage -- the only way to minimise my claw-duggery was by remaining stock still so A.S. Cat wouldn't lose his balance and dig in at an even deeper level of his musculature. Of course I did not always reward him for compliant behaviour and certainly wasn't sorry to see the back of that dogpat when he left.

Even though She has many faults, *extended* bouts of shrieking is not normally one of them. But one evening She screamed and raged at the Lying Hound until a heated conversation disintegrated into a full-scale dog fight over his alleged straying. He'd stood in the middle of her frenzied circling, arms crossed gazing nonchalantly at the ceiling as he far too dismissively leveled a "Hey, Babe, you're totally delusional" while refusing to look Her in the eye when he swore, "There's nothin' going on with the secretary!"

I could smell the lie. She could too – and went for his throat. Missed it sadly but did manage to claw one of the blighter's eyebrows and draw blood. He turned tail and stomped out of the room shouting: "That's it – game over!" Roared down the hallway towards the entrance like a charging bull with me running close behind to make sure he went out the door. Unfit for vermin feed that one!

Shortly after his exit I started sleeping on Her bed. Because she meowed like a distressed feline for weeks, unable to discard the Hound from her mind like so much stinking fish. As a consequence of my beneficence Her catterwailing subsided into barely more than a once-every-few-weeks nose twitch and sniff which I was prepared to live with.

After awhile I started exploiting the actual *training* potential of bedding Her – with respect to Her serving breakfast when I wished it and not when She desired to make it. At an hour of my choosing I would stroll up the entire length of Her body, along her calf and thigh muscles, over her buttocks, straight up the middle of her back to the nape of her neck. There, I would stop and knead various parts with my claws, such as her shoulder blades, if so inclined. Then I would either recline on her pillow or lie spread eagled across the back of her head. Whichever position made her most itchy so She'd start scratching like a dog before moaning, "Okay, okay, you win," after which She would haul herself out of bed and stagger into the kitchen to prepare my breakfast.

Grrr-ow! I wonder – how will Its arrival affect my morning food service now that I've left Her bed?

Late morning: MEGA GRRR-OOOWWW!!! Villainy thy name is human! I have been treated worse than a scalded cat! Have just made a hideous discovery about the whereabouts of my old too-good-for-the-charity-shops food bowl which was replaced only yesterday by the shiny new C-A-T embossed metal eating vessel. After creeping back into the kitchen from under the conifer, I found the house gloriously empty. She and the pigmy lion have flown the coop to who knows where leaving cat alone (good) but unfed (very bad). No tasty titbits of any kind were waiting for me in the C-A-T bowl and now I see it's smaller than my old one (totally unacceptable).

I decided to investigate my living space further and seeing Her office door open, went in. There, in Dog's crate -- oh crime-against-cat most foul -- is my old blue-and-white food bowl and it's *full* of biscuit meal when my steely-looking minimalist receptacle is *empty.*

The horrid new bowl wasn't a special treat after all – only evidence of a shameless act of thievery: She has most squirrelously expropriated A.S. Cat's possession to give to the "spleeny hell-hated bear whelp," which makes Her no better than a "tottering reeling-ripe bitch wolf," to quote one of Her kind long dead. Grrr-ow! Grrr-ow! Grrr-ow! Think I'll move in temporarily with Mad Larissa and live on field mice!

June: Dog Spells *god* Backwards!

Sunday, 1st June: *Exposed secrets*

I am fuming (tip of tail vibrating) while crouched in front of Dog's crate. Seeing my old bowl there again makes me realise -- my world has been turned upside down in only four days when it presumably took God seven to create the universe. It is an unpleasant coincidence that *dog* spells *god* backwards! Before Dog, my future looked bright. Now, a pear-shaped summer's heading my way.

Weather: stormy waters ahead

Hunting prospects: is the pigmy lion a squirrel chaser?

Food: only cause for optimism is Her guilt-driven dispensation of more special treats

Accommodation: unacceptable given loss of office space and unwelcome shared status of house and garden

Dogwatch: rumours of a canine infiltration true if arrival of "little baggage" is reflective of local trend

Entertainment: having to resort to observing Her descent to Dog's level

Her training: years of patient tolerance felled like giant redwood struck by lightning bolt; drastic action required

Plus after spending another night under the conifer, I'm starving. Why? -- because She's taken Dog to the vet and forgot to feed me before she left in a panic about Its "serious medical condition."

29

I was halfway through the cat flap earlier when I heard Her bending the vet's ear about the Chow vomiting. Initially, I retreated from the flap, then thought – no, I'll poke my head back through to see what's going on. Unbelievable! She was in the hallway near the front door trying to stuff Dog into my porta-kennel!

"Good girl, get your little bottom in," She pigeon cooed, to which she squirrelously added, "Sooty won't mind!"

Lies and mendacity: *Sooty wasn't consulted!*

Her cooing ended up parrot shrieking, "Tamba, dirty doggy! What a wet mess you've made!"

Contamination – dog peed in my kennel! Another crime against cat most foul.

That was it; I couldn't take anymore, withdrew my head and ran along the terrace to jump onto the brick wall between it and the end of our drive. A few minutes later, I saw Her leave with my jiggling porta-kennel. Well, within seconds of Her pulling out of the drive, I was sitting in Her office studying the abandoned crate. Its door was open. The revolting smell of warm puppy wee was wafting in from the hallway, her attempts at disguising the desecration of my kennel with *Trees of the Forest* home spray having failed. Nothing escapes a cat's nose.

With them out from under, I had my first good look around Dog's domicile. It's nearly the size of a small garden shed although not as tall. What did I find?

1. My old willow-pattern food bowl, with a few biscuit chunks in it (Being unfed, I helped myself)
2. Another small bowl with water in it (I was thirsty)

3. A blue-and-white throw rug from our kitchen
   (Dug my claws into *that*)
4. A bone-shaped object smelling like ham (Sniffed it)
5. Her little green man washing-up brush (Minus foot)

In a back corner of the crate, I also detected a tiny pile of congealed sick. It had obviously escaped Her notice or would have been hastily removed. Of course, A.S. Cat could see and smell exactly what it was – chewed reeds of regurgitated grass probably coughed up by the puppy in search of fibre. Some "serious medical condition!"

How wondrous are the ways of females. They transform small and insignificant acts of Nature into full-scale theatrical productions. Which has caused unnecessary violation of my cat carrier, not to mention delayed breakfast service. Grrr-ow again!

What a piece of work is woman.

Note: The washing-up brush is a surprise. It was a Christmas present from Her friend Zara who's always trying to turn Her into a homemaker. Which is equivalent to mission impossible. She hates cooking and cleaning. Wonderfully ironic as Dog'll create a hell of a mess.

Monday, 2nd June: *Socialising the lower orders*

I am back under the conifer and it's getting dark. At least it's a balmy evening. Spent most of today outside after the silliness of yesterday. (As predicted, She returned home from the vet's looking sheepish, having been told that Dog was absolutely fine and "just doing what puppies do,"

31

eating grass and upchucking it later. If She thinks I'm using that porta-kennel again, she can forget it!)

Late this afternoon after hanging out at Mad Larissa's, I came back home to find Her sitting with Fat Fiona on the terrace. They were chattering about what She called "socialisation of the Chow Chow." Probably because Fat Fiona is a criminal psychologist.

At one time Fatty had aspirations to become a law professor at "an elite university." But, as She would explain it, her friend is "cursed with a tendency to speak her mind and go for the jugular." Meaning Fatty despises what she herself calls "unadulterated unexpurgated bovine excreta," believing that "action speaks infinitely louder than pontification." Making, She claims, Fat Fiona better suited to the cut and thrust of subduing the criminal element than to the dust and must of climbing ivory towers of academia.

Fat Fiona is also the person who found Mad Larissa wandering down the street one afternoon with her clothes inside out. This happened after the Colonel and Trotsi died. The old lady was living alone and beginning to go walkabout at odd times of the day and night. Upon seeing her on the loose, Fatty brought her back to our house and spent several hours "speaking her mind" on the telephone to arrange for "home visitors." All to ensure that Mad Larissa wears her clothes right side out and eats proper meals. That's when I started dropping in on her as well.

Goodness, what was my point? Prrr! Grrr-ow! Prrr! Even cats lose the plot after living with humans for too long. One forgets how to think catalytically – logically, without wandering off into sentimentality or fantasy.

Oh yes, I was talking about the "socialisation" of Dog. In short I was privy to snatches of Her and Fatty's conversation from my underneath-the-conifer position. They couldn't see me but I could hear them. She was reading from a book about "the 17 ways to socialise your Chow." I remember three in particular:

1. **Accept that the Chow has to be taught to like humans.** *This is most intriguing; it implies Chows are not normal canine bowers and scrapers.*
2. **Touch the Chow's private bits daily.** *Out of order. Dog is a she without any exposed bits but even if Dog were a he and had them, this seems bad form to me.*
3. **Between 10 to 12 weeks, introduce the Chow to others.** *Does not bode well. Dog is almost 10 weeks old. Will others of Its lower order be invited to my house?*

Fortunately, cats are above socialisation.

Friday, 6th June: *Woe is Dog*

This morning She took Dog to the vet for the 4th time since last Sunday when It was coughing up undigested grass. Afterwards she phoned her mother long distance in America to recount all Dog's woes: weepy eyes, mites in Its ears, frenzied scratching (supposedly due to the heat), coughing up a foamy yellow liquid onto the hall carpet (another "serious medical condition"?) and a runny tummy (outside at least). At this rate She and Dog will be visiting the vet over 200 times a year at a cost of several thousand pounds, compared to only a negligible outlay for my 2-3 visits annually. And this won't even cover all the Moaning Minnie calls She'll be making to her mother about them. Dog will not be flavour of the month for long. Prrr! Prrr!

As for Dog's socialisation the "introductions" bit pertains to humans, *not* other dogs. So, guess what? She is scheduling "puppy viewings," and I am invited to observe Dog being paraded around the garden and/or in the lounge, if it's raining, in front of selected adults and children who'll be expected to ohhh and ahhh at the pigmy lion. How horribly crass.

Saturday, 7th June: *Two of a kind*
An unsociable hour of the morning: Grrr-ow! It is far too early in the day for Her to be running around cleaning the house, let alone giving out directives about puppy viewings. Yet that's precisely what she's been doing after head rustling me in my hammock with an odiously cheery, "Hi, Pussycat, up and at 'em." I instantly went back to sleep, only to be ransacked a second time before She scooped me up for deposit on the kitchen counter where I sat tail flapping at the insensitive treatment.

Before I knew it, Dog was brought into the room as well and all the doors leading out of the kitchen were closed. She even locked my cat flap! Virtually imprisoned me before barking, "Okay, guys, let's motor." I could tell She was upshifting into high-flying executive gear, which is always repugnant when one's escape routes are blocked. (What does the Chowpat make of our self-appointed Managing Director of the Household?) Its response was to

34

bounce-sniff around the bottom of the kitchen cupboards without paying Her any attention. One sign of intelligence.

A few minutes later my bowl was dumped in front of me with an ungracious, "Right, Puss, here's your breakfast." Dog by that time was sniffing directly beneath me. During which She put my old too-good-for-the-charity-shops food bowl down by the side of the fridge opposite and blurted out more orders, "Eat up, you two. I'm off to make the bed. Lots to do today." And left us, shut in the kitchen.

I do not eat on command and, it would appear, neither does Dog. It lay down by the hall door and remarkably made no move to touch its breakfast. Preferring instead to put Its head down and close its eyes while I licked my tail.

It wasn't long before She returned, all business like. "Now then..." She breathed out padding around the kitchen, surveying our untouched bowls. "So, no one wants breakfast today?" We had no chance to reply before the crackdown, "Bowls up then!"

Within seconds we were robbed of breakfast as She moved onto her next agenda item. At least she had the courtesy to unlock the cat flap before putting Dog on the lead for its morning walk. Thereafter -- and this is significant in my view -- She found herself trying to drag It out the back door. Despite being a dog and theoretically hot to trot anytime anywhere with anyone, It resisted her advances.

"Come on, pupsydoodle, time for walkies," She attempted gentle encouragement. It flopped onto the floor. "Tamba, get up, c'mon doggy, up you get." She tugged on its lead. It rolled over onto one side. Actually allowed itself to be pulled along the floor rather than rise to Her demands. Its small size couldn't match Her resolve though. She breathed out an edgy "all right then" and swept the puppy up into her arms before stomping out the back door with It struggling to get free. An intriguing exhibition by one so young. Dog's stubborn as well as curious. Now She's frantically trying to brush the Chow after having had the impertinence to issue a "good behaviour" order to me!

Early afternoon: The first canine groupie has landed! No less than "camp-as-20-pink-tents" Sheldon Prattlebury, Her friend who's old enough to be her father and forever giving her "fatherly advice." They used to work together until both were made redundant. Sheldon calls Her "Sweetims" and "Dear Heart." Why, I don't know. Then again, Sheldon's a trifle whifty although he's an avid "pet lover" and *does* bring me tasty treats.

He breezed in after lunch in a "hot pink" shirt open practically to the waist wearing his "absolutely-right, too-tight" grey slacks. More to my liking, he had a carry bag exuding a distinctly fishy odour which is why he made an instant rush to drool over my hammock. "There you are – my delicious Sootster." Gave me the usual chin rub and breathy patter: "Now then, Pussykins, what has Sweetims done to you, by going out and getting a puppy dog? She's a baaad girl, isn't she!"

I love it when Sheldon calls Her "a baaad girl." Plus he reached down into the bag and whipped out a large crusted fish cake. I sat up and gave him a grateful purr.

After which he stroked me from head to tail. I would have rewarded him further had She not grabbed the fish cake out of his hand. "Thanks Shell. Soot'll have it for dinner." She more or less frog-marched Camp as 20 Pink Tents out into the garden before he could say another word.

I don't actually know how Sheldon's viewing of Dog went. Had no interest in watching the proceedings. But on his way out, he stopped by my hammock and whispered in my ear, "Best of luck, Pussycat, they're two of a kind." I didn't think much of his rabid chuckling.

Sunday, 8th June: *Not a husky labrador*

Another viewing today, during which I'd say Dog showed itself up as a dud. Took place late this morning with the two Paddington children from across the street. Little Henry, aged 6, came through the door waving a box of puppy-size biscuits, said his older brother Sylvester, 12, had a squeaky ball and supposedly chewable hide shoe for the Chow. In light of Sheldon's parting remarks to me yesterday, I took myself into the kitchen so I could jump onto the window sill to observe. Could hear all the goings-on through the open back door.

The boys scampered back and forth across the lawn in front of the terrace trying to entice Dog to play with them. Ran up to within a whisker of It and then sped off I-don't-know-how-many times, inviting a chase. But Dog was most unpuppylike -- merely plopped itself down on the grass, taking little notice. They ran around It in ever decreasing circles until a slightly befuddled-looking Henry grabbed what was certainly the chewable shoe from

Sylvester and tossed it a few feet away from Dog. The Chow, who'd been nosing at the grass, glanced up momentarily at the moccasin-like shoe before lifting its back leg for a scratch. Undaunted by the indifference, Henry cried out enthusiastically, "Doggy, it tastes like beef, go fetch." He was panting for Dog to make a move.

After what seemed an age, It stopped scratching, got up slowly and began plodding rather ponderously towards the heelless offering. When It reached the shoe, Dog lay down to give it a sniff. "Go on, Tamba," Henry was desperately encouraging, "fetch the shoe." Finally It picked the biscuit-coloured treat up. Henry beamed. "Here, doggy, bring it here," he yelled, all but wagging his tiny school-boy bum.

Dog sauntered off in the opposite direction before dropping its booty and disappearing into a nearby shrub. Henry was crestfallen. Sylvester was openly disgusted. Muttered dismissively, "She's a girl, Henry." I think both boys were horribly disappointed that Dog is not a husky Labrador Retriever instead of a bear whelping bitch.

Monday, 9th June: *A right posh piece*

She scraped the barrel on the puppy viewing front today! Brought in Drusilla Fence of all people whom She says is "what Eliza Doolittle would have looked like at 75 had Professor Higgins never come into her life," whatever that means. Local scuttlebutt claims Drusilla is an ex bag lady from Hackney who was able to move upmarket to the bungalow down our road because of her uncanny ability to pick a good set of legs when it comes to race horses.

She met Drusilla after finding the old woman's half-Tibetan spaniel Smudge terrorising a neighbour's cat up a tree. I suspect She invited Drusilla over to recruit a future playmate for Dog. Well, Drusilla gave Her a real grilling about the puppy, the significance of which went right over Her American colonial head – per usual.

"She's a right posh piece," I heard Drusilla say over tea on the terrace. "Must 'ave cost you a bob or two."

"Try a bob or four," She'd sighed, all but dripping over a garden chair – probably collapsed under the pressure of baking unburnt scones for the occasion.

That was the start of Drusilla's serious fishing into Dog's history. "So, you say she's got a pedigree as long as your arm?" the East Londoner quizzed Her.

Alleged owner sat up to attention, miraculously rejuvenated and cast a gooey-eyed smile at Dog who was sound asleep on the grass before oozing, "Oh yes, there's a Crufts champion somewhere."

Drusilla was also staring at the Chow, but with the practiced eye of an expert in animal flesh rather than the faulty vision of a slavish idolater. "You saw her parents, did you?" By that time Hackney woman was tapping a wrinkled forefinger against pursed lips.

"Naturally," She chirped in reply, "The father was a real lion king. The mother…well, the poor thing was hounded by a litter of puppies when I saw her, quite understandably she looked bedraggled."

Drusilla turned to fix Her with the steady gaze of a very old Barn Owl. "Who does Tamba take after the most do you think?"

"She's her father's daughter all right," our alleged owner happily buzzed in response, "except for the quirky little mouth. That's her mum's."

Drusilla's eyebrows went up a notch. "You mean the way your precious pup's upper lip bubbles over the lower one?" The old bag lady asked this question rather too sweetly in my opinion, especially given the superior look on the septuagenarian's face.

Ever the proud parent, She remained all wide eyed and fully animated. "That's right, isn't it adorable?"

"Sets a new standard," Drusilla positively purred. She sounded hugely self-satisfied, reminded me of a well sated tabby with canary legs sticking out of its mouth.

Drusilla knows something about Dog She doesn't.

Sunday, 15th June: *A mad bear stripping off bark*
The past week was not as ghastly as I might have predicted -- the crate's proving a saving grace. She keeps Dog shut inside it all day long – except for the closely supervised forays into my back garden for puppy viewings or "to do its business." It eats in the crate, it sleeps in the crate. Thankfully It has not yet done a wee in the crate. And although I'm not happy about Its presence, its impact on my life so far has been "marginalised," to use Her word.

Incredibly, She has actually crawled into Its metal den no fewer than four times to pat and feed Dog treats since the day I discovered my food bowl there. I have observed this inane behaviour from my hammock, which is still in a disgraceful state. It sags so much that I no longer have proper back support. In fact, every time I lie in it, I feel the bottom will give way and unceremoniously dump me onto the floor. But as Her bed and ottoman are currently off limits – and She's taken to closing the lounge door barring my access to the sofa, I have little choice but to use it. As the old saying goes however, every cloud has a silver lining. And mine appears to be the chance to orientate Dog about Its correct position in the household.

Today, She went to buy milk and eggs and on the way out the door, asked me to "take care of doggy." At first, I thought to catnap on Her bed. Then it struck me – I had the furry cabbage all to myself. At which point I felt quite buoyant, energetic and up for a stroll past Dog.

As I approached the crate, I could see It lying down facing the entrance while engrossed in chewing a small bone. She'd stuffed the bone through the wire mesh before leaving. Curiously, the Chow seemed completely unperturbed by Her departure. Didn't give Her a second glance or cry out pitifully at the sound of the front door closing. Which attitude is worthy of further consideration.

As soon as I entered the office, Dog began to devour my presence with its eyes. I ignored It but started a very slow wander across the room past the crate towards the unoccupied ottoman directly in my path. Out of the corner of my left eye, I saw It get up and walk towards me with a stilted little aren't-I-the-greatest gait before sticking a chubby paw against the crate wall. The Chow's nose was twitching, ears aping small antennae searching for signals from an unknown planet. Planet being A.S. Cat.

I took no notice, looked straight ahead as if Dog did not exist. My peripheral vision picked up the canine's nose and ears vibrating in an overwhelming desire to communicate. I gave It not an eyelash flutter nor the slightest whisker tremor. Which made Dog pant vigorously and scratch the wire of its cage with one paw as cat strutted by oblivious. Taking great pains to titillate without brushing against Dog's overly large mitt. Inviting more scratching -- until It reared up on its hind legs and attacked the barrier between us with both bear-like paws.

I continued inching forward in show-cat stance, tail and head erect, both eyes glued to the ottoman ahead. Thereby converting Dog into a fluffy mass of rampant pawing punctuated with mouse-like cries.

Squeak! It craved acknowledgement. No scrap did I offer.

Squeak! Squeak! Its scratchings escalated into frenzied digging at the crate wall. At which point I stopped and sat down in Sphinx pose with my back as near to the flailing canine as I dared. Dog descended into a demented panting of desire. I heard It running back and forth behind me with all the passion of unrequited love.

Woof! The pigmy lion yapped a would-be bark. I was unmoved. Dog woofed again. I sat like stone. Which prompted It to recommence slashing the crate like a mad bear stripping bark off a tree.

In the midst of the melee, I detected the hum of a car pulling into the drive. Her returning. Without looking at Dog, I gracefully arose and stepped up the pace of my journey to the ottoman in time to hop up onto it, lie down and curl up into a perfect and serene ball of consummate cattiness before She opened the front door. Dog was yapping furiously, circling the crate like a lunatic squirrel. I meanwhile was engaged in a delicious pretence of sleep made more delectable by Her rush into the office demanding an explanation for all the noise.

"What on earth's going on here?" She was trying to emulate a concerned mother as she knelt down to stick one finger through the crate's mesh to calm Dog down. It continued puppy-dog woofing in my direction.

Through half-closed eyes, I saw Her glance over at my peacefully reclining body. "Pussycat, what's wrong with pupsydoodle?" When I offered no reply, she gushed, "Sooty, you're so good, aren't you! All this racket and you take it in your stride. What *would* I do without you?"

"What indeed!" purred I ever so smugly.

Wednesday, 25th June: *A dull and boring wench*

I have completely lost interest in orientating Dog. Making It scratch, whimper and bark was enjoyable at first. I could revel in working It into a froth of raspy yapping while appearing to sleep peacefully in my hammock or innocently on the ottoman whenever She rushed into the office to calm It. It was magic sending the Chow and Her into tailspins – until today. For today Dog showed Its true colours as a monumental bore.

Late this morning when She left the house, I went into action: jumped down from the hammock, sauntered into Her office and launched another strollpast. Dog stopped chewing its after-breakfast bone but didn't get up. Abnormal. It should instantly have started scratching at the crate with its usual excitement. It didn't. Instead, it rested Its head on its paws and looked the other way!

A.S. Cat moved in closer to the crate. No reaction. I moved even closer. Dog kept its head down. Cat stopped practically opposite Dog's nose. It raised its head but *not* to look at cat. Pointed Its nose at the unoccupied ottoman. Not only that – It got up and sniffed its way to the back of the crate where It lay down and shut its eyes!

I was admittedly nonplussed by such un-Dog-like behaviour. Cat decided to make contact with the crate. Actually rubbed my flank along its wire mesh. I didn't like the bumpy feel against my ribs but I was sure such proximity would get a response.

It did – Dog got up, turned round the other way and lay back down again with – how dare It! – its back towards me! It didn't glance once in my direction. Nor have the decency to make a single nose twitch.

I was sorely affronted and became even more so at the pronounced and profoundly irritating snoring coming from the beast. That's when I realised -- Dog is fundamentally a dull and boring wench, undeserving of cat's further attention. Wanderings past Dog's crate are suspended.

Sunday, 29th June: *Confrontation on the terrace*
With the benefit of hindsight, halting my strollpasts has proved a fatal error. In their absence the past few days, Dog has "calmed down" in Her eyes. The house has become much quieter in the mornings so that today, She decided Dog was "grown up enough" to be let loose outside. Now, my life will be truly miserable.

44

I was snoozing on the terrace after breakfast in the warm sun, on the verge of leaping into a pool of field mice when Her voice shattered my pounce: "Pussycat, where *are* you?" She was bird singing amid the sound of the back door opening. "We're coming outside."

Grrr-ow, I tail swished and lifted my head to signal I'd heard her dulcet tones, in the hope She'd button her beak. I didn't much like the sound of "We're."

But before I could put my head back down, She began squealing like a pig, "Doggy, doggy! Stop! Come back here!" Suddenly, the pigmy lion, who's about 1 ½ times bigger than me now, was upon me. Ran right across my body. I hate being sniffed up and down like a juicy bone. It even had the audacity to bat A Superior Cat in the face!!!

So unexpected was the attack, it took me a few seconds to muster my defences, during which Dog was wriggling up for another charge. From a supine position on my right side, I managed to unleash a murderous growl. Followed by a paw swipe at Its bear-like face.

"Impudent baggage," I hissed. "How dare you!"

Not the slightest put off, Dog batted at me again.

"Away with you, foul beast," I spat, waving both claws in Its face a second time. But all the baggage did was fall upon me in a forward roll. While all this was happening, She stood frozen on the terrace, clearly at a loss.

"Tamba, come *here*!" she ordered, trying to sound commanding in a voice bellowing with anxiety. "Sooty, it's OK, she's only a baby, she won't hurt you, Pussycat," imploring me to take it easy on the furpat.

No chance of that, my tail swished. I growled as I sprang up, determined to cast aside my 17 years and reclaim the heady days of full-blooded tom cattery. "I'll teach you a lesson, minxy heathen."

The fluffy perpetrator remained unbowed, running around me like an overgrown mouse with delirium tremens. I lashed out with my claws. It stopped, ran the other way. Worse, it seemed fearless. Which infuriated me. Dog was quiet, too, its silent antics making me more livid. From its ridiculous tail wagging, I'd say the Chow was revelling in the encounter.

I hissed. My back fur stood on end as I went for a knock-out swipe, running my claws right down the front of Its craggy face, from forehead to mouth to dig into its lip. It tried pulling away. My claws sank deeper into its jowl. But goring Dog was not easy. Like trying to score a sheep's pelt. My nails got entangled in its woolly coat.

This made Her shriek: "Sooty, stop, stop!" She rushed across the terrace to intervene. I tried withdrawing my claws in the hopes Dog would continue pulling away so I could tear its lip. But alas She grabbed hold of the puppy and practically sat atop it to prevent any damaging movement. Next, She put one arm around me and with the hand of her other tried to dislodge my claws.

I hoped It would madly squirm as She tried unpicking my talons from its face. It didn't. Had the sense to lie still, shrewdly accepting its predicament. I yearned to see fear and trepidation in those small sharp eyes. But they only looked quizzical, as if It were purely an observer rather than the target of an assault. I curled up my claws more tightly to make their removal harder.

"OK, Pussycat, let go of doggy." She tried sounding calm though I sensed her terror at my powerful position. If my whiskers had been the spines of a hedgehog, I'd have speared Her hand as she struggled to extract my nails. Unhappily, they weren't. Against my will, She released It from my deadly clasp.

Incredibly, Dog said nothing throughout the struggle. No sound, not even a pant, had passed Its lips even when my claws were deeply embedded in them. Dog simply looked at me with the same aggravating curiosity it showed the first time we met. Disturbingly catlike. An attitude which could present serious problems for me.

Monday, 30th June: *House Rules are announced*
This morning at breakfast She announced the adoption of certain House Rules. These are actions which Dog, any future playmates and all humans must take--or not take-- out of respect for me. Which proclamations are nothing more than political window dressing to make Her feel less guilty about ruining my life, notably:

No 1: The dog will never ever be allowed on Her bed; that will always be the cat's special place. *Mindless -- I have left her bed which fact She never mentions!*

No 2: All visitors will have to speak to, and pat, the cat first. *In principal ridiculous -- cats are by nature not dependent on being either spoken to or patted by humans.*

47

No 3: **The cat will always, without any exception whatsoever, be fed before Dog**. *Good in theory, sham in practice -- She feeds Dog treats throughout the day!*

No 4: **The dog will not be permitted to gang up on the cat in cahoots with other dogs**. *Totally meaningless and irrelevant -- Dog's not permitted to run around with other dogs in or near the house.*

These rules are a fraud – purely attempts to impress her friends and pacify me about Dog's arrival. Plus I heard Her whisper to a friend that I am quite old; thus there's no telling how long they'll have to be enforced in reality. The sad fact is -- She's paying less and less attention to fulfilling *my* requirements on *my* timetable. The only glimmer of hope is Her stated intention to enrol Dog in Obedience School. However, I am sceptical about the probable impact of that; it's become very apparent -- Dog has a thick skin and very possibly, a thicker skull.

July: Unadulterated Canine Excreta

Friday, 4th July: *A second Day of Infamy*

Triple GRRR-OW! Not only am I a betrayed cat but a crippled one lying in acute pain under a shrub in the back garden. My right hind leg is useless. It hangs limply from my body, meaning I'll have to hop along on the other three to go anywhere. Birdnapping will be out of the question, pigeons will crap on my terrace and magpies will dive bomb my garden. As for removing the pesky squirrel from my domain, vile Dog has ruined carefully laid plans. My summer will be worse than pear shaped!

Weather: won't be able to enjoy good days

Hunting prospects: nil

Food: no appetite

Accommodation: won't even be capable of jumping into falling-apart sheepskin hammock

Dogwatch: will now require a single-minded focus on the squirrelous pupsydoodle

Entertainment: nothing on the horizon

Her training: suspended due to cat's serious injury

The only thing greater than my physical discomfort is my fury at the cheek of Dog chasing the Stinking Squirrel! It didn't ask permission. Just cavalierly sped across the boundary of common animal decency. Worse, She thinks I bolted up the tree because of the Chow! As always She fails to grasp the truth even when the truth slaps Her face!

The disaster happened earlier this afternoon when I was lazing around the terrace ignoring a Bobbin' Robin hop-by to keep an eye on the squirrel. Unusually at that time of day, he was ferreting around the lower garden.

I hate that squirrel. He steals my birds (except for the magpies!) and doesn't hesitate to drop acorns on my head. I want nothing more than to take the vermin down. As I watched its back and tail vibrating upwards under the conifers, I had wondered -- could this be my lucky day? Could I dash down the hill fast enough to catch the nut stasher unawares? Which thoughts were interrupted by Her dragging Dog outside.

The Chow made a move towards me until She yanked It backwards, scolding: "Leave Puss alone, we're going for a wee." Dog followed, straining to keep me in sight. I ignored It, preferring to watch the squirrel shift his position. He was intently crunching on something, seemingly unmindful of the eyes above.

I got up very slowly, crept along the edge of the terrace to make my way down the stone steps leading to the lower garden. The squirrel was to my left. My plan was to surreptitiously but surely slither down the steps, then snake my way along the right-hand side of our property between the shrub border and boundary fence to take up a more advantageous place behind the greedy critter. From there I could have executed a long-jump pounce at his back, after acting with consummate stealth to stay outside his peripheral vision of course.

As I crawled intently down the stairs, I heard Her coaxing Dog to "do its business." The squirrel looked up but dismissed them as any imminent threat. Didn't see me either, continued munching. I reached the last step and just as I was about to slink down onto the grass and under the shrub to my right, She shouted, "Tamba, no, stay!" When I glanced up, I saw the wretched beast careering down the hill towards MY squirrel! Leaving me no choice but to catapult myself forward in a diagonal leap towards the crackerjack who took off like a bullet up the trunk of the taller of our two conifers. I chased after, not about to let Dog get there first.

The odious creature began chattering loudly at me from several branches above. I was sure his tail was waving, *bet you can't catch me, you decrepit mouser*, as I pursued him up the tree. She started pleading with me to stop. "Sooty, come down, Puss. Doggy won't hurt you," As if I'd had the slightest fear doggy could! I heard Her clatter down the stone steps as I inched my way up the trunk, gripping the bark as tightly as I could. Dog yapped below.

I was half way up the tree when the scrappy varmint darted up to higher ground. I figured he'd attempt a flypast to the shorter conifer. So I pounced onto a branch below in readiness to paw swipe him as he took to the air. But the blasted branch cracked, plummeting me to the ground. I watched the furry rodent peer down at me with his fuzzy flat tail twitching in delight

Thud! My hind quarters hit the grass followed by the branch with the rest of A.S. Cat's unfortunate body wrapped around it. I lay stunned. Within seconds excruciating pain seized my right leg. Rage at Dog was the only thing which kept me conscious. That and the shame of being felled by a stinking squirrel and rotten tree who couldn't keep its branches up.

Predictably She set upon me like a manic poodle. "Oh Pussycat, what *have* you done to yourself?" When She made a move to whisk me up from underneath the branch, I growled menacingly. Much preferred Nature taking stock of my battered body to Her. "Okay, Puss, take it easy." She withdrew her arms and stood back up, entreating me to "stay put."

I knew I'd taken a very bad fall but equally, I was sure no bones were broken. We cats are of faultless anatomical design, quite elastic and flexible with the capacity to survive drops from very great heights – far greater than humans in relation to our size. I lay still, breathing deeply, trying to relax while She hurried to reclaim Dog. It was barking up the tree, unconcerned by my grounding. Had She stopped to analyze that fact, even Her human brain might have divined the real motivation for Dog's headlong rush down the hill. Her assumption that I'd turned tail and run in fear of Dog was preposterous. Embarrassing! How infinitesimal is human understanding of truth.

By the time She'd collared Dog and hiked back up the bank with It reluctantly in tow, I'd regained sufficient strength to pull myself out from under the feathery branch to slowly and painfully crawl into the nearest large shrub.

Several minutes later She returned, tripping down the stone steps to call me. I didn't respond. Thank goodness, She decided to let me be and retreated back into the house. My leg and knee throbbed but not enough to put me off falling into a deep sleep devoid of evil women and foul-smelling vermin. Now I'm awake, they're all back and I hurt like hell!

Saturday, 5th July: *Doing what men do…*

Grrr-owwww! Despite being shot up with painkillers and airlifted onto the lounge sofa by Her, I feel like the loser in an extended alley-cat fight. Only the real alley cat is not Dog or the Stinking Squirrel but Her, and her version of the events leading to my downfall.

When early this morning I finally struggled up off my bed of fallen leaves under the shrub where I'd lain since yesterday's debacle, I was exceptionally hungry and thirsty. Every bone in my body ached. I could hardly walk. In short, I was in a dreadful state. But somehow I dragged myself out onto the grass and made the tortuous journey up the hill to crawl through my cat flap, which almost finished me. I'd prayed She wouldn't be waiting on the other side; the thought of any histrionics from Her at such a low point in my life was insupportable.

Alas, as soon as I started through the flap, Her face loomed large in front of me. "Oh, Sooty, thank heaven, you haven't popped your paws after all," She was on all fours on the kitchen floor, watching my progress and aching to pick me up. By some miracle she didn't, allowing me to wriggle into the kitchen in my own time. Not a pleasant experience. It ended in my half-hearted attempt to sit upright, injured leg splayed across the floor, in a most ungainly and uncatly stance. Made Her take a sharp intake of breath at least.

"Holy cow, Pussycat, what a mess you're in." She shook her head at me and stood back up before picking me up from behind. Wrapped both hands around my chest to hoist me up onto the counter where she set me down front feet first. I lay there crouching low to the counter top as She initiated some gentle prodding. Mind you, I knew what was coming next – a visit to the vet's surgery. Which I dislike intensely. It always seems full of rampant waggers and putrid pawstompers. Too often they beat my carrier with undisciplined tails and make the surgery smell like a canine rubbish tip.

Sure enough, she announced her intentions. "Right, Puss, we're going to the vet." Emphasised with a no-nonsense head pat. I laboured to pick myself up off the counter. Had the forlorn hope of leaving the house before being subjected to a cacophony of unruly dogs.

"Oh, no you don't," she started stroking me a bit too vigorously, "don't even think about it. You can't possibly go back out into that cold cruel world." I was sure She was ignorant of the irony of that statement – never imagining I considered the "cold cruel world" to be right in front of me. Nor could She appreciate that my physical pain was as nothing compared to the anger and remorse I suffered at Her subsequent fallacious accounts of my accident. First to the vet's receptionist ("I think doggy gave Puss rather a fright!") and thereafter to the vet himself. She chattered on and on about my having been "felled by a puppy" as if cat's fall was the subject of an award-winning TV drama.

Fortunately, the vet is a shrewd judge of animal character who speaks to me and not over me as people often do in front of animals and children. "So, then, Sooty, what have you done to yourself, Old Boy?" He asked after She'd brought me into his office. He peered at me through the porta-kennel door while sticking one of his fingers through its grate to give me a nuzzle. Put his face down next to mine and grinned conspiratorially: "I don't see how a mere puppy could scare you up a tree, Mister." He winked before opening the door to give me a thorough going over.

I bestowed upon him my slinkiest purr. At long last the voice of male sanity was defending my honour; the vet had penetrated the clouds of faulty female logic under which I'd been living for weeks. In that moment I yearned to give him a juicy field mouse. Instead, I cooperated fully with his meticulous efforts to examine and x-ray my bruised and battered body.

Afterwards when She'd gone off to arrange another appointment, he leaned down so we were eyeball to eyeball. Began massaging me around the neck. "So, Pussycat, what were you *really* doing up that tree?" It was more of a comment than a question, made with the crinkle of a smile because he needed no answer. I knew the vet knew what She was incapable of knowing – that I was doing what men do in the thrill of a chase!

Monday, 7th July: *Plagued with guilt*

Prrr! Her misapprehension about my accident has had one salutary effect – She is plagued with guilt. Believes herself to be at fault. Which she is, having lost control of Dog although It only theoretically scared me up the tree, setting the scene for my mishap. Nowhere does the role of the Stinking Squirrel enter Her consciousness. Blissfully for me, She remains ignorant of what actually happened.

In this respect I am forced to admit -- except for the squirrel, the only other being on earth who might know the absolute truth is Dog! Interestingly, because Dog is still little – and unschooled, She does not blame Dog for my injury although She believes Dog provoked the incident. Which misinterpretation is bearing fruit.

Cat is now the focus of Her attention. She has given me tuna chunks in brine today which I actually prefer to spring water. And I've had cheese with every meal since I limped back through my cat flap. Dog is on a very tight rein. In the house It is never off the leash in my presence since I have great difficulty walking. In addition, She is telling people that Dog must start Obedience School "as a matter of urgency" although on reflection it is not Dog who needs it most.

Tuesday, 8th July: *Opportunities for mortifying Dog*

Prrr! Prrr! Prrr! Another slender ray of light at the end of the rat tunnel of my Dog-ridden life. In order to get It out of the house, out of my garden and away from me as I am so gravely incapacitated, She has decided to take Dog to "an adorable little park" a few minutes' drive from the house for walkies twice a day.   And, oh harbinger of better times to come, during its initial foray early this morning, the puppy got away from Her and ran out the entrance onto a road over flowing with peak-time traffic. The only reason Dog didn't become mash on the motorway, according to Her, was because It sped into a traffic accident and all the rush-hour cars which would have been doing 65 mph down a 50 mph road were at a full stop.

The experience appears to have affected Her far more than Dog. She spent the entire morning hyperventilating a minute-by-minute rundown of the almost-but-not-quite-fatal mishap to her mother, Fat Fiona, Dog's breeder ("Is this normal Chow puppy behaviour? How can I put a stop to it immediately?"), assorted neighbours and a total stranger collecting money for *Save the Children*. All the while Dog was nonchalantly sniffing around its wire-mesh pad as though nothing extraordinary had happened.

Every time She relayed her tale of high-pooch drama down the portable phone line, she was shaking her head and panting like a dog: "It was awful, utterly mortifying. Two smashed up cars, a motorcycle lying on its side, an ambulance, fire engines, police everywhere -- although no dead bodies on the road, thank goodness – and doggy runs into the centre of it all."

Not quite mortifying enough, I would say as I lie here in my newly repaired fleece-lined hammock. She placed me in it, reverently – along with a chunk of medium cheddar, before taking Dog back to the park for its afternoon walk, from which they have not returned. Which inspires me to fantasise about the Dog disposal potential of the "adorable little park" and busy routes around it. One possible flea in the ointment does buzz around my brain however and that is -- It too could have nine lives.

<u>Wednesday, 9th July</u>: *Petty-minded greed*

GRRR-OW! The salutary effects of special treats have worn off. Today She exhibited a reprehensible display of petty-mindedness and greed in response to results of my x-rays which confirm torn ligaments in my right knee and the presence of bone fragments floating around my kneecap causing swelling and cat's "undoubtedly severe pain." Both of which I could have told the vet!

"What do we do now?" She had enquired all respectful and intently listening while leaning over to stroke my back in concerned-pet-mum position at his office this morning.

"Surgery," he shot back. "We'll go in and take the frag-ments out." He declared this with rather more enthusiasm than I deemed fitting.

Her response was incredulity. "You want to do surgery on a 17-year-old cat?" She enunciated each word very slowly as if the vet had an English language problem.

The vet persisted, "Sooty may end up arthritic if we don't." She stiffened to her full height, arms folding across her chest.

"Sooty already *is* arthritic." There was suppressed irritation clinging to every syllable as if she were talking to a difficult client, trying to be tactful when firmly opposed to "unreasonable demands." The vet leaned forward. His hands were palms down on the examination table. I'd have said he was digging in for a pitched battle.

"If we don't do surgery," he said evenly. "Sooty may have a bad limp for the rest of his life."

"Hmmm," She was frowning in my direction. "And just how much is this *surgery* likely to cost?" She's already complained to Fatty about the vet's "absurd" charges.

The vet did not look at her. "A few hundred pounds, I would have thought." Her eyes opened wide, shot a you-can't-be-serious scowl his way. I could tell from many years of experience – the vet was sinking in status, from consultant to lowly supplier with the wrong price in mind. Which prompted Her to answer, she didn't want a cat of my age "to endure the risks and rigours of surgery" preferring to "let Nature take its course." Her nose was in the air as she said this, and it was with a finality the vet knew better than to challenge.

Mega grrr-ow! When I consider what She paid for Dog, and all the carry bags of Its stuff, Her response was – no, IS -- scandalous. What She really means is: *I'm not forking out all that dosh for an aged moggy.* Serves her right to be oppressed by a high-maintenance dog and uninsured "rescue cat" in his dotage.

Saturday, 12th July: *More catlike than canine*

This afternoon I was privy to a most thought-provoking exchange between Her and Fat Fiona on the subject of Dog. Fatty dropped in for coffee on her way to some kind of meeting about "the hooligan element of the neighbourhood." Came over beforehand to hear how Her new business is doing.

Until recently She had gone out to work every day. This left me to do as I pleased. I could sit and sit and sit and continue to sit anywhere for as long as I wished, without

Her wanting a "cuddle." Could sleep on my back without interruption or Her trying to tickle cat's tummy. Wander off for squirrel chasing without being interrogated as to where I was going. Total peace and serenity all day long without Her around to disrupt my schedule.

But soon after the Lying Hound left, She began staying at home to work. It was exceedingly tiresome having Her underfoot; she constantly asked for advice.

"Soot, what *am* I to do?" she would meow sitting on the swivel chair in the guest bedroom which had been converted into an office. I'd be trying to sleep curled up in a ball on the ottoman. She would start whining, "Soot, what am I to do?" I could imagine creases running across her forehead. Then She'd become insistent, "PUSSS, speak to me!"

After which she'd drone on about "being downsized" and "shafted by corporate politics and backstabbing." Or escalate into raging when She'd get up off her chair and dart around the room waving her arms and parrot-shrieking: "How *dare* they make a whole department redundant! How *dare* they announce their biggest profits in history on the back of our job losses!" She'd be shaking her fists. "We should sue the bugbears!" Or something like that.

By that time I'd have given up any thought of a nap and raised my head in her direction. More than likely, to see Her eyeballs popping out of their sockets. Or teeth baring as Her arms swiped at the air with claws in full extension.

If I hadn't known her so long, I would have headed for the nearest tree. But since it was only Her, I calmly retreated into Sphinx pose, eyes shut as normal, and pretended to listen. Eventually, She'd run out of steam. In refusing to become embroiled in her ranting, I effectively brought Her to heel. Granted, the process was wearing but my slight deafness made it bearable.

These work-related tirades went on for weeks until "clients" began to give her "consultancy contracts" which thankfully put an end to most of her squawking. Or at least reduced the shrieking to the clicking of her nails on a computer keyboard or smarm cooing over the telephone.

Admittedly, I've never fully understood what she does. She calls it "marketing" and "advertising" and it gives her the wherewithal to provide me with food and shelter, after a fashion. I can only recall one even mildly intriguing statement She's ever uttered about her work — when I overheard her tell someone that "The bird's eye commercial is the cat's whiskers."

Anyway, Fatty dropped by to see how She was getting on. Never found out though because all She talked about was Dog. I'd made a point of limping into the kitchen to eavesdrop, which elicited a minor mention of my improving health at the start of the conversation.

"Ah, here's the wounded pussykins," She regarded me sympathetically as I hammed up an impressive three-legged entrance. The prospect of more tuna chunks in brine was too delicious not to invite Her pity. She practically sprang off the kitchen stool to lift me very gingerly up onto the counter beside the window looking out onto our garden. Since the accident She has placed a small pillow there for me to soak up "healing rays" of the sun after breakfast.

"There you go, Soot, you rest while I chat to Fi." She set me down on the pillow. I looked up at her, my tail a question mark. As if on cue, she went to the fridge and took out a half-eaten tin of tuna chunks in brine. "All right, Puss, because you're still poorly," She said forking a few chunks into my minimalist but shiny bowl. The delectable flavour of tuna peppered with guilt can dull almost any ache, and I could easily listen in on their conversation.

"I don't know what to do about doggy, Fi," She complained, slumping down onto a stool at the breakfast bar facing her friend who was perched opposite with both elbows on the counter. "She's not like other puppies, you know," She bleat, bleated. "Won't play with any of the toys I gave her except that ridiculous washing-up brush." More bleating. "I take her to the park where other doggies want to play and the little madam runs off into the traffic."

I saw Fatty stifle a smile.

"Here I am trying to make friends with these local dog walkers," She was frowning now, "and mine doesn't give them or their pooches the time of day. It's awfully embarrassing. If doggy's like this now, what will she be like when she's older?"

Fatty sucked in her cheeks to appear serious when her dancing eyes said otherwise. "Even more aloof and independent, I imagine," she replied without hesitation.

She was not amused. "Fiona, this is not funny."

Squirrelous policewoman only shook her head, "You're the one who wanted a Chow -- a self-willed, stubborn creature unimpressed by the human species!" Fatty stopped and lasered Her face before adding, "Which by the way sounds like someone else I know!"

"Not at the age of 14 weeks!" She snapped, ignoring her friend's remarks.

"No? Is that what *your* mother said when you were a screaming baby refusing to breast feed or go to sleep -- 'she's too young for all this'?"

"Fi, this is a dog we're talking about!" She dug in her heels. Fatty remained unmoved.

"Ah yes, but a dog chosen by you, a dog who behaves like a cat! No wonder Freud had one!" Fatty was emphatic.

I must admit – Fat Fiona's psychoanalytical powers do impress at times. What she said today fascinates. I've never heard of a dog who behaves like a cat. And yet, I too have detected a certain catness about Dog in its unexpectedly curious nature. If it is so, and Dog is truly more catlike than conventionally canine, is this a good thing or a bad thing?

Tuesday, 15th July: *Mulling things over*

Well, well, well, Her efforts to enrol Dog in an obedience training programme have hit a brick wall. Two schools actually turned Dog down today. I heard Her moaning about it to her mother over the phone.

Apparently, the first one She contacted said they preferred *not* to handle Chows because "such dogs are so uncooperative they lower the company's overall success rate in a very competitive marketplace." The second recommended one-on-one coaching only and they don't offer any. "We've never had a Chow go above Level 1 in a group situation," they told Her. Chows, they said, are "enormously stubborn" and, they warned, Dog might have to repeat an introductory course several times before It will "even agree to sit down."

Not surprisingly, She has mentioned nothing to me about finding a reputable school for Dog. No doubt because I was present when Fat Fiona told Her the Chow breed is "intelligent by nature but prone to mulling things over before obeying." I distinctly heard Fatty say, "When it comes to training, Chows can be convinced – but *only* if owners use effective arguments." Which is tantamount to predicting Her unmitigated failure with Dog as She is more prone to "executive orders" than "effective arguments."

Friday, 18th July: *Stick tail down throat*

Great cause for celebration, She's telling anyone who'll listen! Pink-tents Sheldon has come up trumps and found Dog, and Her, an Obedience School called – stick tail down throat – *Pooch Perfect*. It reputedly has "an excellent reputation for training even the most resistant, retarded and/or recalcitrant of canines." That's a direct quote from a leaflet She received today, which she insisted on reading out to me and Dog. The leaflet came in the post along with pages of other drivel about a so-called Good Doggy Scheme, The Canine Code and all the training accessories She and Dog will need for the course. Not to mention tips for cleaning up dog pee and poo. None of which is necessary for a cat.

Pooch Perfect has even sent Her recipes for "fool-proof" training treats, including one for something called "Good Doggy Fish Cake."

"It's made with tins of tuna and sardines, Puss," She couldn't help telling me, "You'd love it, wouldn't you!" I was not then – nor am I now - enamoured by the idea of Dog incentivised with tuna fish. Tuna is a treat for A.S. Cat and A.S. Cat alone in A. S. Cat's considered view.

Saturday, 19th July: *An insurmountable problem*

More junk mail from *Pooch Perfect* this morning. Specifically, a "To Do" list for Dog's first class next week. Now She's freaking out over their instruction to bring a favourite non-squeak toy along for "supervised play and retrieval exercises."   It presents "an almost insurmountable problem," She says – "Dog doesn't like toys, Puss, what shall I do?" It's true too. I have seen Her shower Dog with hard rubber balls, tennis balls, dog chews, nylon bones, cast-off knee socks, old bedroom slippers, pieces of kitchen carpet tile and myriad other useless artefacts which She has purchased and/or salvaged from the rubbish bin, only to have every one rejected by the hard-nosed little Chowpat.

All the cast-off "toys" are currently stored in a clear-plastic stack-a-box labelled, oxymoronically, Dog's Toy Box. The only item in which Dog shows a germ of interest is Zara's little green man washing-up brush. Dog stole it out of the kitchen cupboard under the sink before chewing one of the feet off and likes tossing it over head. But I can't imagine Her taking a dismembered dish brush to

Obedience School, and in any case based on Dog's reaction to the Paddington boys, I don't see *retrieving* ever being on *Its* To Do List.

Monday, 21st July: *Something in common*

She is getting down and dirty with Dog to prepare It for Obedience School!   This afternoon I actually witnessed Her grovelling to discuss training toy alternatives with the puppy. I was sitting somewhat stiffly in the hallway outside Her office when she stepped over me carrying the toy box, normally stored in our hall alcove. Dog was sitting behind the crate door staring into space. She plunked the box down in front of It, got down on her hands and knees and began sifting through all the bric a brac. Fired off a "You can forget the dish brush" salvo at Dog first, adding "No way we're taking *that* mangled manikin!" All with a don't-you-dare-disagree-with-me expression on Her face and in her voice. Which Dog met with a blank stare.

Naturally Her demeanor softened when She saw me observing. "Hello, Puss, how're you doing?" She got up and walked over to me. "Right, let's get you out of harm's way," and lifted me carefully up into the hammock where I rested my chin on the edge facing the office doorway so I could monitor the vetting process. She returned to her task and knelt back down on the floor facing me with the toy box rising up to mid-thigh level. Hovering over its contents, She began tossing one "toy" out of the box after another in Dog's direction, inviting some sign of canine approval. But nothing sent It into paroxysms of joy – not a bone-shaped rubber rattle or over-sized acorn of a Kong (unstuffed with peanut better).   Nor the ham-scented nylabone She waved at Dog. The most It did was scratch or lick its private parts in response.

In the end She had to choose. "Since you have no stated preference, we shall take the red ruff rope bone for non-destructive chewing." Which prompted Her to extract a red-and-white rope-looking thing which She held up to her own face. "It can't bounce and won't squeak," She announced triumphantly. The Chow turned its back on Her and wandered off for a sniff. Not remotely excited by the red ruff rope bone.

If anything, Dog remained inscrutably Chinese throughout Her attempted sales pitch; no hint of any emotion whatsoever escaped its craggy face, or none of an easily identifiable sort. If I'd been pressed to describe Dog's attitude, I'd have said It thought Her inconsequential. Something we would have in common.

Tuesday, 22nd July: *Near fatal exposure*

What a carry on! After all Her preparations opening night at Obedience School was a "total fiasco." Her words, not mine, after dragging Dog back through the front door on a specially designed *Pooch Perfect* training lead with slip collar.   She returned home noticeably indignant that a "dirty white Labrador called Schmuck practically ripped doggy's ear off in a merciless and unprovoked attack." She and Dog had only just arrived and were sitting among 19 other puppies and their owners in the church hall hired for the class.

"Shocking," She blurted out to me within seconds of slamming the door shut and seeing me curled up in the hammock. I could tell She was livid by the way she thumped her jacket onto the coat rack.

Throughout Her harangue Dog simply bounced down the hallway as normal, making a beeline for me of course before She yanked it backwards (I remain a severely injured party in Her eyes and She isn't prepared to risk any more accidents). I couldn't see any signs of attempted rape or pillage on Dog's person in spite of Her contention of Its near fatal exposure to total disfigurement. Frankly, I fail to understand Her completely humourless disposition about it all.

Wednesday, 23rd July: *"Virtually untrainable!"*

Ah ha! The reason for Her inordinately black mood last night is revealed. I heard Her talking to Fat Fiona only minutes ago on hands free in her office and have now determined the real cause of Her fury. It transpires that a Pooch-now-definitely-Imperfect instructor asked her publicly if She'd read the new American best seller about personality matches between dogs and owners. Well, She hasn't and therefore was pig ignorant about the fact it lists Chows as the second stupidest breed in the world: "virtually untrainable." Which fact the instructor was only too happy to share with everyone in the class.

She was suitably miffed (personally affronted, if you ask me) by the implications until Fat Fiona, who *has* read the book, pointed out that its author had used *obedience to humans* as the main criterion for judging a dog's intelligence. Fatty's generally cynical views on human nature have accordingly dismissed the text as so much "unadulterated unexpurgated bovine excreta," which pleases Her no end.

Friday, 25th July: *Not smarter than US!*

Her obsession with Dog's IQ is driving me crazy. She's been ranting on about the pitiful personality study for the past two days. Even dropped by my hammock this evening on the way to Her bed (which I still refuse to frequent) to share Fatty's comments on the subject. Dog was in its crate and the office door was shut.

She flopped down on her knees beside me and began rubbing me under the chin as a prelude to unleashing Her clearly burning questions about Dog's (and by association Her own) intelligence. "Look, Puss, I know you're not thrilled about puppy but do you think doggy's a dummy?"

My tail flapped back at Her in disgust but She read what she wanted into it and prattled on: "Well, I don't think pupsydoodle's clueless either, regardless of what that ignorant psychologist says. Neither does Fi. You know what *her* advice to me was?" She was head patting me by this time while my eyes were half shut.

"Fi said, 'Given the deplorable state of mankind, ask yourself whether a dog is more or less intelligent if it obeys idiots before getting too worked up about the assessed mental capacities of yours.'"

At that point She stopped patting me and shoved her nose into mine. "Puss, do you think doggy's simply smarter than us?"

If She could have accurately read my whisker twitches, she'd have been left in no doubt about cat's answer: *Dog may be smarter than YOU but certainly not US!!!*

Note: I hope Fatty's perspective on the dumbing down of Dog does not dispel Her shame at having a puppy who has publicly cocked a snout at *Pooch Perfect*. For it was also amusing to learn that Dog kept putting its bum in the instructor's face while straining to join the advanced class next door.

<u>Saturday, 26th July</u>: *Behind the butchy exterior*
A day of Supreme Enlightenment about Dog whose mien and behaviours I have been scrutinising very closely. During every waking hour in fact, since my tree fall and severe curtailing of daytime and nocturnal activities. Leading me to conclude:

1. Dog is **exceptionally curious** -- for a dog.
2. Dog is **not unintelligent** – It does not pay slavish homage to Her (even though She climbs into the crate with it routinely).
3. Dog **looks tough** with a scowling face and lion-like ruff around its neck and shoulders. There is nothing feminine about Dog who stands its ground like a defiant baby bull.
4. It exhibits **"male wanderlust"** (always angling to go walkabout).
5. Dog is **catlike:** aloof, self-contained and reserved.

6. Therefore, Dog is also **remarkably quiet**, a very un-female trait which I do not mind (That It *does* bark at strangers is quite beneficial).

So, prior to today's happenings, I would have labelled Dog a "butch bitch," a female but not a girly dog. Nor a pitty-pat paw-tapper or incessant wagger at the sight of Her or other humans. But Dog is *not* what It appears. Not judging by today's events in the back garden when She left It unattended to check on Mad Larissa who was found wandering around last night without any clothes on.

Shortly after She'd gone out, three very-low-flying jet fighters passed directly over the house (subsequently identified by Her as planes doing aerobatics at a local air show). The whole building shook; I thought I'd vibrate off my window sill pillow into the kitchen sink although the deafening sounds irritated more than unnerved me.

Not so for Dog. It went berserk, actually cried out in abject terror. As the jets passed overhead, the Chow began bearing down on the back door like an angry rhino.

When a running tackle didn't open it, Dog thrust its woolly head in and out of my cat flap repeatedly until It ripped the entire apparatus out of the door! But the Chow still couldn't get into the house because my "dirty white" cat flap, fractured but intact, was strangling its neck. Even I was beyond mega grrr-ows at the ludicrous sight of Dog barking its grotesquely misshapen noggin off as It flailed about in the shrubbery. Adding to the fracas, upon her return She walked into the kitchen and let out a piercing scream at the gaping hole in our door.

"Good Lord, Puss, what's gone on here? Where's doggy?" She was frantic then lapsed into parrot shrieking at sight of the cat-flap-encrusted pupsydoodle thrashing itself back and forth across the terrace at high speeds.

I can only conclude -- behind Dog's butchy exterior is only another manic poodle like Her!

August: Frying Eggs on the Terrace

<u>**Friday, 1st August**</u>: *Prospects are mixed*

Weather: It's so sizzling hot that "eggs could fry on the terrace" (Her words) and Dog needs ice cubes in its bed

Hunting prospects: dreadful as a result of my tree fall; mouse sports on hold; recovery period prolonged by inadequate veterinary care due to Her diversion of funds into *Pooch not-so-Perfect* training

Food: improved -- more tuna dispensed by Her during extended guilt trip over cat's "ghastly accident"

Accommodation: office still uninhabitable because of Its presence in the crate with Her bed remaining off limits although once-badly-torn sheepskin hammock acceptable

Entertainment: despite Stinking Squirrel debacle and temporary inability to pursue posh puss down the road, potential amusement is provided by Her and Dog

Dog's behaviour: bully-girl tactics substantially toned down following Its terrorisation by low-flying jets, impact of heat wave and Her enrolment in Obedience School

Her training: moving forward as a result of the unanticipated impact of my injury

What a week – I'm glad to see the tail end of it, except for the burning sun we've had every day which, I'm pleased to say, brutalises Dog. Its loathing of hot sunny days is directly proportional to my own ecstatic bliss at being lasered by its rays. Dog can't bear my bliss. Even when set free for a wee, It heads for the nearest shrub and burrows deep within the leaves. Which keeps its relentless scratching out of sight as I cast my eyes over the garden from the safety of my kitchen-window-sill pillow.

As always, there is what She calls "a downside"; in such weather Dog sheds its fluffy coat constantly. The unending fur-storms are tiresome although birds love them. They swoop down on the woolly tufts littering our grass and spirit them away to the eaves of the roof, very likely for nesting. Which circumstance could be extremely advantageous once I'm back on all fours. But I'm not and the high-rollers who sully my garden are often magpies.

Come to think of it, though -- bird napping is too much hard work these days, sport for the young and foolish. After all, what's the point of dirtying my paws on a bunch of black-and-white spivs? No, when I rise again to the occasion, it'll be to take out much bigger game than a few magpats. And I know *exactly* who I mean!

Note*:* Dog has been lying low since the flypast. Is off its food, seemingly remains unhinged by memories of roaring jet engines. What a wimp! A pity my cat flap didn't strangle It. Speaking of which, installation of a new one was attempted by Fat Fiona's retired policeman father. Who should stick to straightening out riff raff as I now have to enter and exit by a crooked door -- as if being three-legged weren't challenge enough!

Monday, 4th August: _Fireworks dementia_

Dog's suffered another panic attack -- over fireworks set off this evening in a neighbour's garden. I saw It go mad in Her office. As soon as the rockets started, Dog began salivating profusely and whimpering in its crate. Started running around in circles, sporadically pressing Its nose against the mesh while flailing the wire with its paws. She'd been working at her desk and tried some soothing shushes. Dog responded by hurling itself against the crate, at which point She leapt off her chair and hurried over to it.

"Calm down, calm down, little pupsydoodle, Mummy's here!" She tried speaking softly as she opened the crate door and began climbing inside. Held out her arms to comfort the distressed Chow, which action unwittingly provided an escape route. Out Dog flew – squeezing past Her like a greased piglet.

Before She could extricate herself, Dog had scurried underneath Her desk and wedged its chunky frame into an impossibly narrow space between the desk's back panel and office wall. Within seconds the puppy had disappeared into nothing more than four bear-like paws on half haunches. "Tamba, come out, come out now!" She commanded, having dropped down onto all fours to crawl in after Dog. Which order Dog ignored, seemingly being stuck. She looked back wildly in my direction. "Oh, Soot, what do we do now?"

"Don't look at _me_," I purred, resting my chin on the side of the hammock. I did throw Her a whisker twitch or two and cocked one ear to mirror her concern albeit through half closed eyes. I refused to accept any responsibility for

75

the rising chaos although was quite enjoying watching events unfold.

She got up from the floor, moaning, "Doggy, what *am* I to do with you?" Then began struggling to move the desk which was weighed down by a mountain of files, Her computer, printer, telephone and fax machine. "I can't possibly shift all this." She was huffing and puffing, straining every muscle to pull the piece of furniture out from the wall. It wouldn't budge.

"Blast, I'll have to remove everything," She groaned. That's when Dog's laboured panting converted into the sound of frantic scratching. I saw its front legs had gone missing. Did It think to dig itself out?

She didn't wait to find out. "Oh gawd!" she groaned again and tore out the door. But even after Mr Paddington had come over to help Her move the lot and return Dog to its crate, the Chow carried on running about, whimpering and drooling. The fireworks continued and no amount of pigeon cooing could allay Its demonic paw bashing.

She tried calling the vet; the line was constantly busy. Beads of sweat broke out on her forehead. Even Her cowlick stood on end, a sure sign of acute stress. "Damn, I'll have to ring Her Ladyship," She sighed, deep lines crossing her brow. "Her Ladyship" refers to the rather imperious Lady Regina Tattersley DBE who used to play bridge with Her mother when her parents were living nearby before they moved to America. Lady Tattersley owns two standard poodles who once suffered from what Her Ladyship calls "fireworks dementia," defined by her as "the extreme behaviour of over-bred dogs who cannot abide loud noises."

The story is -- Lady Tattersley's poodles (two fluffed up ponces from all I've heard) became so crazed during a Guy Fawkes celebration held on her estate, they started eating a 200-year-old mahogany door. Lord Tattersley was inclined to grind the poodles down into premier bone meal afterwards until Lady Tattersley pleaded for mercy, promising such "aberrant behaviour" would never happen again. The incident became the talk of Her mother's bridge four, which is how She and I heard about it.

However, being a lover of pedigree poodles, Lady Tattersley is not partial to "under-bred Colonials," according to Her mother. Thus, She who is unversed in the social graces required to engage aristocracy was very nervous about ringing the lady uninvited. Hence Her delaying tactic of pacing the office, clutching an address book with white knuckles, until feverish glances at the high-kicking front legs of Dog spurred Her on. "Right, Soot, I *must*," she glanced at me for reassurance before closing the office door. Perhaps She didn't want anyone to witness her lowly approach to a member of the British Upper Crust.

After some muffled conversation, the door reopened. She walked out visibly unburdened. The cowlick was down, Her I-can-do-anything attitude back. "It's all down to Valium and Mozart, Puss," She exhaled with relief and renewed confidence. "Thank heavens, we've got both!"

A few minutes later, as soft music welled up inside the room, I was not chuffed to see Her press a small cheddar cheese sandwich through the crate door into Dog's mouth before popping one into Her own. Grrr-ow! You'd think She'd have given *me* one for all my moral support.

Tuesday, 5th August*: You wicked little bitch!*

PRRR Maximus! A deliciously hot day! Thankfully not hot enough to keep Her and Dog home from Obedience School this evening despite Its demented behaviour of last night. Not to mention, She's become disenchanted with *Pooch Perfect* after four weeks. Says "they're not delivering the promise." More like, She's miffed about Dog's published lack of intellect. She's definitely infuri-ated by the sniggers She says circulate around the church hall every time the instructor says, "And now it's Tamba's turn,*"* made more galling by *Pooch Perfect* staff forever insisting "There are no bad dogs, only owners unable to communicate properly" (I don't totally disagree with that as it happens). In short, Dog is performing badly or more precisely, as She complained to a fellow dog walker today:

- Dog will not "focus" on doing what She asks.
- Dog won't sit long before lying down, and when It does, lies with its bum in the instructor's face.
- Dog keeps trying to join the Advanced Class next door.
- Dog refuses to stand at attention, sits instead.
- On the recall, Dog goes to anyone but Her.

"It's all so embarrassing," I heard Her grumble, typically adding, "The classes aren't exactly cheap either."

Upon reflection I find Her allegations of Dog's non-compliant behaviour pause for further thought because in our back garden, It *does* obey. Well, as long as treats are in sight. Yet, in class where She also uses treats, the uncooperative canine is said to flop down on its tummy, preferring to be dragged across the floorboards on its side than be seen obeying Her before a group of peers. Prrr!

Friday, 8th August: *Dancing attendance*

The heat wave continues. Just as well. Soaring temperatures keep Dog under bush so cat can fry three-legged self on terrace unmolested, as I did this afternoon. I am still stiff and sore from my injuries although the throbbing in my leg and knee is dulled by Her renewed attentiveness. Yes, She's been distracted by Dog's fireworks dementia and training issues. But generally speaking, I am benefiting from my mishap:

1. She feeds me on a **more predictable schedule**, with more ham, cheddar and tuna chunks on the menu.
2. She has **banned DOG** from the kitchen so I can eat there in peace. (It must pass through on a leash.)
3. She **lifts me up onto the kitchen counter** whenever I glance up. I need meow only once for a lift back down. (Ditto for the hammock)
4. She has purchased **a new sheepskin cover** for my hammock, along with a catnip toy (although catnip's a bit plebeian for A.S. Cat).
5. She has **placed a large pillow on the lounge sofa** for my use and hoists me up onto it at a mere glance.
6. She has bought a **new litter tray** so I don't have to struggle outside to wee or poo (and ordered Fat Fiona's father to straighten my crooked cat flap).
7. This afternoon She bought a **"top-of-the-line" fleece-lined black-watch plaid cat igloo** for my use

on Her bed. I have chosen to reward Her by returning to her bed as She will lift cat up onto it and escort cat back down to the floor whenever required.

My convalescence could be worse. Mind, I'm a trifle put out She hasn't returned me to the vet for another check-up given she rushes to ring him if Dog so much as sneezes.

Saturday, 9th August: *Dog prefers tossing*

More scorching weather. Had to vacate the terrace early this afternoon -- my paws were frying in the sun. She kept cool in cut-off jeans and a halter top. Dog scratched and panted so furiously in its crate that She sprinkled several trays of ice cubes over it. The Chow spent the rest of the afternoon licking them or tossing the odd one over its head. I have noted -- Dog prefers tossing to chewing things. In the garden It can lose what it tosses – I see a bone or whatever sailing backwards over Dog's head at a high rate of speed to land in a bush or neighbour's hedge and that's the last time Dog or She sees it! I don't think She appreciates how much tossing Dog does, and mistakenly writes off missing bones as buried! Its tossing strikes me as potentially problematic somehow.

Tuesday, 12th August: *A human-gous huff*

My ears are inflamed from Her slatings of *Pooch Perfect*. Fat Fiona's must be, too. She's been in a human-gous huff about how She and Dog were publicly humiliated this evening at Obedience School. She rang Fatty to complain bitterly about how they were "ordered" to go into a side room on their own with the *Pooch Perfect* founder Miss

Dawgsbody for "special handling." What riled Her was the public announcement beforehand that the 72-year-old dog trainer is only brought out of retirement in "emergency situations," Dog and Her being one of them. Dawgsbody supposedly said: "We cannot allow one disobedient canine to set a bad example for others on an ongoing basis and therefore on occasion certain dogs are removed from class temporarily to receive special attention." After which both were escorted out of the hall making Her absolutely livid until Dog inadvertently got Her own back.

At the end of the class they were allowed to return to the hall to "show what Tamba had learned with extra *Pooch Perfect* tuition." She was asked to demonstrate the recall. As usual Dog did what Dog wanted – ran right past Her and out the nearest door where, fortunately, It was intercepted by a *Pooch Perfect* assistant.

Dawgsbody didn't want to end the class on a disobedient note. So insisted on repeating the exercise with herself commanding Dog's return upon Its release by Her. Well, Dog not only didn't come back to Dawgsbody, It ran in the opposite direction and out the other door. By which time Dawgsbody was less than overjoyed with the Chow and yelled out loud, "Come back here, you wicked little bitch" in front of the entire assembly of owners expecting a *Pooch Perfect* performance.

"It was a disgraceful thing to call doggy," She said all indignant to Fatty. "Totally unprofessional – *Pooch Perfect* are supposed to train dogs, not slag them off in public!"

Dog is now back in its crate for the night and looks not the least perturbed by its *Pooch Imperfect* branding.

Funny, I can't say the same for Her – She's at her desk ferociously pen tapping a handwritten letter of complaint which, She has told me, will demand a full apology for Dawgsbody's "insulting behaviour towards a client."

Friday, 15th August: *Shopping not buying*

Her dripping-with-diamante friend Zara, Dog's dish-brush benefactor, called in this morning. Is desperate for Her to go out to dinner with "a distant cousin" (name is Arthur) as a favour.   Zara tells Her he's "a 40-something South African businessman, divorced, no children" who appeared on her doorstep late last night "out of the blue" and that she and fourth husband Roger have a previous "unbreakable engagement" Saturday night; therefore would She "please Dahhhling" take over as hostess tomorrow evening (Zara to happily pay for dinner for both). Alleged owner has reluctantly agreed, only after making Zara swear there's "no hidden agenda" to replace the Lying Hound. I am not convinced but Zara did say Arthur's "an animal lover."

She met Zara (current husband Roger followed two divorces and one suicide leaving her with multiple millions and stepchildren whom She says may one day conspire "to take Zara out") at a health farm during Her Big Business Executive days enjoying the corporate high life when we lived in a large detached house with housekeeper.   Zara was between husbands and they struck up a conversation while waiting for what I'm sure She called "a seafood wash." Zara apparently introduced herself as a "very-high-maintenance, supremely-well-kept woman," the total opposite of Her -- a financially independent, self-made career type who has sworn (I've heard her) to "die a thousand deaths rather than be kept or accessorised!"

Incredibly they "hit it off instantly." She says it's because they agree about "not being born to spend days cooking endless meals, washing dirty socks or kowtowing to a species who fundamentally only want women to come naked and bring beer!" Of course, it's obvious to me – their strategies for achieving this common goal differ dramatically, and Zara is forever advising Her to lighten up because "too much work makes a dull girl" and "there are many many many men and oh so very very little time."

Secretly, I think Zara wants to bring Her down to the "high-maintenance" woman's own level by finding Her a man to "play with." Explains Zara's concerted efforts to arrange "blind dates," which gets Her back up. Especially given She's "done with men," or so She says, while Zara's forever saying, "Dahhhling, don't get your knickers in a twist – we're shopping not buying!"

Zara would never be my cup of cream (dislikes cats intensely). On the other hand she *has* proven to be a better judge of character than Her, having voiced reservations about the Lying Hound early on. "Far too many loose ends with *that* one!" Zara told Her after meeting him for the first time. Now Zara's pushing Her to do more shopping.

Saturday, 16th August: *Lots of "uck" words*

Pity about Arthur. He was quite presentable really, in a crisp white shirt and khaki-coloured trousers. Much slimmer and trimmer than the Lying Hound. I couldn't detect any nicotine fumes or see any chin stubble on his face. Nor hear a squawking mobile phone anywhere. He arrived with an enormous bouquet of flowers and box of dark chocolate-covered caramels (Zara must have briefed him about Her sweet tooth). Most impressive (by Her rapturous look), Arthur brought a fresh hambone for "the wicked little bitch."

A date made in heaven? Not a chance! She made a cardinal error – gave Dog the hambone *before* dinner, when She and Arthur were having drinks on the terrace. The furry tosser ran off with it and moments later, with one manic WHOOSH, sent the bone flying over Its head with the force and trajectory of an African Hottentot spearing lions. Only it was Arthur who took the hit. Right between the eyes.

Within seconds blood was gushing out of the poor chap's nostrils onto his no-longer-crisp white shirt and all over our garden furniture. The terrace was vibrating with lots of uck-sounding words I've never before heard come out of Her mouth! She couldn't even offer the unfortunate victim an icepack, having forgotten to fill up the trays after showering Dog with cubes a few days ago. Her blind date ended up a "dog's dinner" in Accident & Emergency.

Sunday, 17th August: *Shopping spree suspended*

She was in a distinctly foul mood all day. Very tight-lipped with me as well as Dog, whose bloodied hambone was binned first thing amid Her muttering, "Pets should not cost so much time and money." That's rich! What about the acute bugstration alleged owners cause pets? Dog meanwhile seems totally oblivious to the havoc It's created. When let out into the garden, It bounced up and down the terrace as if sniffing for its lethal weapon.

I surmise Her bad mood was aggravated by lack of sleep (She didn't get home from the hospital and driving the ex-replacement-hound prospect back to Zara's house until very late). Add to that -- having to make homemade scones (hates cooking, avoids like plague) promised to friend Carol's little girl whom She invited over this afternoon for yet another puppy viewing.

With Dog in Her bad books (serves Her right for getting one!), anything involving the injurious canine clearly annoys. Makes me purr although I resent being tarnished with the brush of Dog's depravity with a hambone. It's not my fault the Chow drew blood with said bone or that She went without dinner last night and received a call from Zara earlier which, I gather, has suspended all shopping sprees.

As I watch Her smoulder over yesterday, I have to wonder -- what kind of bones has *She* tossed into the faces of men before Arthur?

Tuesday, 19th August: *Spitting slugs*

Spitting slugs this morning, She is! Miss Dawgsbody has replied to Her complaints about *Pooch Perfect*. I was napping in my hammock when the post arrived and She seized upon a particular envelope, ripping it open and hissing through its contents like a venomous snake.

The *Pooch Perfect* missal (Naturally, she read it to me) was rather wordy and pedantic and one bit really got Her goat where She paused and spat out "arrogant cow." Dawgsbody claims that *She* is the main reason for Dog's failure at school. The letter said something like: "We know from years of experience, a dog's performance is *always* a reflection of the owner's. Any unresolved training problems lie at the feet of the owner – not the dog or *Pooch Perfect*. We suggest you read a few books on dog psychology before progressing any more training of yours. Also, ask yourself the question, 'What more must I learn to bond with my Chow?'."

No Obedience School for Dog this evening.

Thursday, 21st August: *Fabricating the truth*
Today, She told her mother that she and Dog have opted out of *Pooch Perfect's* training course because Dog could not withstand the "oppressive temperatures" in the church hall during the current heat wave and She consequently will not force Dog to go back there until the autumn. A squirrelous fabrication of the truth!

Monday, 25th August: *Reading my mind*
For the first time in weeks I have felt like walking on all fours. Even She noticed. "You're looking better, Puss," She told me this morning after I'd hardly limped into the kitchen for breakfast. When She leaned down to lift me up

onto the counter, I took a leap at it myself – and landed with my injured leg a bit askew but more or less in line with the others. She was surprised, warned me not to do that "quite yet" before patting me on the head and going into the fridge for my food.

She was right. As I looked down, I didn't relish the return journey. Then sensed Her watching me from the fridge door. "Don't worry, Soot, I won't let you go back down the way you came!" For once She read my mind correctly. After I'd eaten, She lifted me up off the counter and put me down on the floor.

At dinnertime I noticed one of the two stools usually tucked away beneath the breakfast bar had been moved into the space which would normally have been my launching pad for the counter. This means two smaller leaps instead of one big one on my part. Prrr! Prrr! Prrr! Alleged owner *is* responding to training after all.

Tuesday, 26th August: *Gross misconduct*

Training of Dog is now a critical issue in light of Its gross misconduct towards me on the terrace this morning. Which occurred after She'd come back into the house from playing with Dog, to answer the phone. Feeling fitter, I had gone outside to supervise It in Her absence. Barely had I finished crawling through the cat flap when the Chowbat jumped over me during a mad rush across the terrace! (From time to time It goes temporarily insane, whizzing around my garden in circles.)

In crouch position I looked up and saw Dog do a forward roll onto the grass ending in a somersault before it bounced back up to gaze at me rather too pointedly. Its purple tongue was hanging out and its ears were twitching non-stop. With its tail flapping back and forth like a feather duster, It was preparing its next assault.

Prompting me to arch my back and verticalise my tail to intimidate. Which only incited the canine cannonball to shoot forward as I steadied myself for a massive jolt. Luckily, She tripped out the back door at that very instant and swept me up into her arms while Dog veered off its headlong course to avoid crashing into Her ankles. "Oh no you don't, you monster," She all but barked, "Leave our puss alone. He's recovering from a nasty accident, no thanks to you!" Her anger smelled delicious. Peppered with remembrances of the Hambone Incident perhaps?

Dog did a hairpin turn on the terrace and sped off towards the bottom garden. "Right Puss, back inside with you, I shall deal with doggy." The rising temperature of Her irritation warmed the cockles of my heart, along with the sight of her striding off to collar Dog after she'd returned me to the kitchen.

Wednesday, 27th August: *A scorned cat avenged*

The night is sultry and I am lying across the back steps licking my paws with inordinate satisfaction after having exacted my own punishment of Dog for its wayward behaviour on the terrace. When She took it out for walkies this morning, I set off for the office where, as hoped, the crate door was wide open. *I too shall deal with Dog,* I recall purring to myself as I stalked into the centre of Its living space and crouched down.

88

Never before have I felt such joy at the prospect of elimination. Indeed, after emptying my bladder of every last rotten-cabbage-smelling drop of urine in it, I could only turn around and marvel at the perfect symmetry of the wet puddle creeping outward from the middle of Dog's bed. A short time later, after I'd settled down on the kitchen pillow and She had returned with Dog, I purred contentedly at Her predicted exclamation of disgust, "Dirty doggy, if it isn't blood on the floor, it's more bloody wee!!!"

PRRR MAXIMUS! There is no finer emotion than that of a scorned cat avenged.

Saturday, 30th August: *A godfather for Dog?*

Lunacy reigns! She has gone "round the twist," as Her mother describes people going crazy. This afternoon She called her young godson Rupert Scallionrapper and asked him to become Dog's official godfather even though Rupy (Her pet name for him, poor lad) hasn't yet met Dog and his mother Marigold is terrified of canines (cats too). I guess this is Her way of giving Rupert, who's "desperate for a pet," the vicarious thrill of ownership.

Rupert and Marigold are invited to an "investiture ceremony" to take place here tomorrow at teatime. She plans to give Rupert a certificate which he is to sign confirming he will "do everything in his power to inform, educate and entertain his goddoggy throughout the course of her life and, in the unlikely event of Her premature death, take full responsibility for providing food, accommodation, training and instruction in high morals and good behaviour." She read the whole thing out to

Dog in the office. From my hammock I could see – It's not impressed. It stayed curled up asleep in the crate. Snored throughout. All sounded like doggerel to me, too.

Why does Dog need a godfather? Is She trying to offload responsibility for Dog's discipline to a third party? Perhaps the godfather is supposed to whip Dog into submission although in fairness She's never lifted a hand to me and Rupert is only 7. Up to now the only godfather I've come across is a gun-toting Italian type in films She watches at least once a year on television – mostly late at night between Lying Hounds.

Sunday, 31st August: *Mummy's fainted!*

Rupert arrived for the investiture dressed in his Sunday best, "excited to bits about meeting his new goddoggy." Like the young Paddingtons he was weighed down with presents for Dog. Obviously, She's not told Rupert that Dog's a non-starter in the toy department. Mother Marigold trailed behind, tittering nervously and, as ever, begged him to "warn me where pussycat is" so she could avoid me. Whereas Rupert is small and dark haired, Marigold is like a tall but underfed Golden Chinchilla cat. Her dense mop of curly hair is the colour of rich cream with seal brown and she has a rangy figure kept slim by an overwrought disposition.

Rupert and I have a gentlemen's agreement. He doesn't pull my tail or whiskers and I allow him to pick me up and hold me for as long as he likes. This keeps mumsy out of his hair and Her out of my fur during their infrequent visits. For all Rupert is a child, he treats me with respect.

As I am discovering is the case with Dog-related events, the ceremony did not go according to plan. I was banished from Her office where it took place, to prevent Marigold from becoming hysterical; she became hysterical anyway. First off, Chinchilla woman had a sneezing fit. Turns out she could be allergic to Dog's fur. As She was presenting the certificate to Rupert, Dog escaped from the crate because the little boy hadn't closed the door properly after crawling inside to get acquainted with It. The new goddoggy headed straight for Marigold (amazingly cat-like) who frantically climbed up onto the desk. Dog must have interpreted her flight as an invitation to chase. Jumped up onto the ottoman beside the desk and put Its paws on top of Marigold's feet. Which sent Marigold into a screaming fit before she fainted, after which She asked Rupert to fetch his petrified parent a glass of water from the kitchen.

Rupert came rushing out of the office yelling, almost gleefully I might add (fully appreciating the exciting aspects of a family crisis), "Mummy's fainted, Mummy's fainted. Have to get her something to drink, Sooty." Spoken with the resolve of a young man on a life-saving mission. I followed him into the kitchen where I leapt up onto the counter to watch him fill a tumbler. Rupert took it as a chance to comment to me about the basic nature of his new charge.

"Tamba's not a normal dog, Sooty," his youthful brow crinkled with perplexity. "She doesn't play with toys."

I purred softly in reply to this profoundly accurate observation, by which time the glass was full. As he prepared to leave the kitchen, Rupert looked back at me and asked the most searching question which She has yet to answer, "How come *you* don't have a godfather, Mr Cat?"

Precisely.

September: Jumping through Hoops

Monday, 1st September: *The honeymoon is over*

With Her and Dog off my back for the night, I am sprawled across my hammock, with one paw dangling over the side, feeling quite upbeat for a change. The rosy glow of dog ownership is no longer so rosy to Her. She hasn't said as much to me. Wouldn't, would she! But the fact is – She had a good old moan to Fat Fiona over the phone by her bed earlier this evening on the back of the less than highly successful investiture ceremony.

I am *not* sleeping with Her tonight. Varying my routine keeps Her suitably appreciative when I *do* put in an appearance. "Stay mean, keep 'em keen" as humans say. However, I got the gist of most of Her whimpering to Fatty as Her bedroom door was, and remains, open (She lives in hope I'll join Her).

"Oh, Fi, my *whole* life is run by the dog" She started whining about one deadly-dull woe after another -- the "relentless walkies," "outrageous cost" of never-ending trips to the vet, Dog's daily grooming, vacuuming three times a week and worst of all, Its "utter rejection" of toys. She made a meal of the toys as "unappreciated sacrifices" in light of Her current uncertain financial position as newly self-employed.

She also yowled about being "horribly disappointed" that Dog never comes to Her for cuddles.   What did she expect?   Dog's a Chow.   Chows don't "do cuddles,"

93

especially with humans who crawl over them like fleas. I mean, really, what self-respecting animal wants a human inhabiting their cage?   Man-made hovels are crowded enough without excess baggage.

Anyway, She catterwailed on for ages.   Obedience School is an "unmitigated disaster," She admitted.   No surprise there. Dawgsbody's right, *She's* the real problem. I can see that.   Then it was onto the "nightmarish" Hambone Incident. By all accounts Zara has crossed Her off her A-list.

Well, yawn, yawn, whiners can put anyone to sleep and I was on the verge of nodding off when I heard my name mentioned. "Really, Fi, it's all so stressful. Thank good-ness I have Puss – *and* he's well enough to jump back onto my bed these days."

Prrr prrr prrr! I will overlook Her head-in-the-sand inter-pretation of the reason for cat's return to bed because the glad tidings are -- the honeymoon with Dog is over. Reality is finally sinking in. Who knows -- the days ahead may be better than expected:

Weather: still warm enough to keep Dog in the bushes
Hunting prospects: on hold although I'm thinking about a new strategy for taking the Stinking Squirrel down
Food: paws up – meals on time and lots of special treats
Accommodation: improved with lounge sofa pillow, new igloo plus higher levels of owner service to support cat's recovery from horrific injury and thwart any assaults from the hambone tosser

Entertainment: bordering on never a dull moment with emergence of a second drama queen (Dog) in the house
Dog's behaviour: irritating given the potential for my grave bodily harm; interesting given Her bonding failures
Her training: am getting Her back in line as evidenced by her putting foot down with Dog on the terrace

Tuesday, 2nd September: *Perchance to dream…*

PRRR MAXIUMUS! I'm sure I saw the elusive posh puss this evening when I was on the terrace after dinner watching a wood pigeon preening itself on the branch of our neighbour's tree. It suddenly flapped its wings and lifted off. I reared up to scan the surrounding gardens; that's when I caught sight of a slinky silver tabby creeping along the top of a brick wall located a few gardens down the hill from ours. I'm sure it was Posh Puss. She's the only such cat around. Has "exquisite eyes." I haven't seen them but She has, during a visit to Mad Larissa's awhile ago. The posh puss was sitting on the pavement in front of the old woman's house.

"She looks like a white tabby spray painted with silver and black rings," She raved to me about "the absolutely stunning cat" she'd seen with "sea-green eyes." Being so taken with it, She made discreet enquiries and discovered the owners had only recently moved in at the end of our road. She popped in to welcome them and reported back to me. The tabby's name is Petronella and it belongs to a 30-something couple with no children, the Fenbinders. Apparently, both work on the Stock Exchange and are very busy "rolling in dosh" since they drive his and her silver Mercedes, own a villa in Mauritius and have a Jacuzzi with gold-plated taps in their bathroom.

She is quite adept at assessing other people's socio-economic status starting with the pedigree of their pets, nearly always gilding the lily of mine. "Sooty is what you'd call a tuxedo cat," She tells people. I notice She leaves out the "quite common piebald" mention although not my resemblance to a certain black-and-white moggy associated with a leading cat food brand. "Sooty's markings are exceptional," She will inevitably add about the "perfectly symmetrical white mask" on my face. I always shut my eyes and go into Sphinx pose when She's waxing lyrical about my pedigree since in truth it can be reduced to two simple words, "animal shelter."

Back to Petronella. The silver tabby used to live in London until her owners decided to "get out of the rat race." I remember Her saying. "You'll have to show her the ropes, Puss, make sure she doesn't run into any foxes." This followed Her revelation about Petronella's "fatal flaw" i.e. her owners from abroad, before the Fenbinders, had her de-clawed "to save all the upholstery" (severely reducing her capacity to save herself, which fact was conveniently ignored). She is gravely indignant about this while I confess to thinking, at least there won't be another cat chasing my squirrel! Not that I would wish de-clawing on any cat; it's like cutting off a human's hands.

That was months now but I'm sure it was Petronella on the wall today. Even from a distance, I could see her fur was dense and silky, her paws large and rounded. Prrr prrr prrr! Her pads must be a wondrous rose-pink. I ache to get my nose into those shiny white whiskers. Bugstration! My gammy leg prevents even A Superior Cat from doing more than feast his eyes on an object of obsession. When Petronella looked up at me this evening, I turned my back on her.

Ah well, per chance to dream of a silky-soft silver tabby with sea-green eyes running through tall grasses to meet a black-and-white tuxedo cat without the shadow of a limp.

Thursday, 4th September : *When might She die?*

Am keeping a low profile since encountering Petronella; that is, am steering clear of the terrace and staying under cover when going out into the garden. I don't want pussy willow becoming too curious too soon. It would be ghastly meeting up before I'm fully recovered and leaping up walls at a single bound. I must be patient. All comes to he who waits. Guess I'll have to be content with watching Her and Dog's bonding failures. She sounds like a broken woodpecker complaining to all and sundry about them.

Oh yes, the investiture of young Rupert as Dog's god-father is proving micey. Problem – Marigold hates dogs and cats and wants absolutely no responsibilities for one, even on a paper-only basis. However, Rupert is taking his new role very seriously and wrote Her a letter to that effect, which arrived today. She read it out loud to me. It was rather endearing! Rupert asked when She might die so that he can take over Dog's education and training!

Did Marigold read the letter before Rupert sent it?

Friday, 5th September: *Strangled by a Dane*

Pooch Perfect is to be given another chance! Dog is going back to Obedience School. She announced this after dinner. Hmm! Does her decision have anything to do with Miss Dawgsbody's death which She learned about only this morning? She saw a news story about her demise in "a bizarre accident" while scanning our local paper after walkies. Sounded anything but sympathetic when She mentioned it.

In fact, She boomeranged out of her swivel chair screaming "Dawgsbody's dead, she's dead, doggy, dead – strangled by a Dane," with sheer delight in her voice. Even Dog raised its leonine mug at Her animated state.

Evidently Dawgsbody was found tied to tree, in the death grips of a fully extendible dog lead wrapped several times around her neck with a Great Dane (hers) sitting patiently at the older woman's feet, the "victim all but garrotted," said the paper. Experts surmise that during a frenzied squirrel chase, the Great Dane sprinted around the tree half a dozen times, inadvertently strangling its hapless owner who had somehow got caught between the trunk and the dog who was taller than her.

Miss Dawgsbody's unpremeditated (?) manslaughter was welcome news to Her: "Just desserts if you ask me, a fitting end to a wicked old bitch!" She was hissing the last bit and looking directly at Dog who did no more than put its head down.

Meow! What are the implications of such attitudes for my own wellbeing?

Tuesday, 9th September: *GO FETCH THAT BONE!!!*

Unbelievable! She spent all day preparing Dog for its return to Obedience School! Rescheduled two client meetings to go out shopping for Cumberland sausages and, more unbelievable, all the ingredients for Good Doggy Fish Cake. She is an *I hate to cook, can't cook and won't ever cook* fanatic, bound by a self-proclaimed solemn oath to "never ever not in a million years" cook a roast before the age of 40!!! Despite even the Lying Hound's promise of a no-expenses-spared week at a 5-star hotel in Paris, She has resisted any temptation to drown an unsuspecting spring lamb, pig or cow in mashed potatoes, mushy carrots and lumpy gravy! Yet, she intends on making Good Doggy Fish Cake for a canine???!!!

Late this afternoon She attempted to take Dog through training exercises in the hallway positioning me to observe from the safety of my porta-kennel. Predictably, as soon as Dog came out of the crate, It strained for a snuffle at cat but soon lost interest when it couldn't penetrate the moulded plastic of cat's "safe house."

Extraordinary! A few minutes later I saw Her kneel down in the hallway, to my right, and push Dog into a sitting position on Her right with the toy box behind. Next, She reached into it and extracted the previously rejected Red Ruff Rope Bone and waved it enthusiastically in Dog's face. "Here, Tamba, let's play tuggies." She was bouncing up and down on her knees. It only cocked its head and gave Her a vacant stare.

"Like this, Tamba!" She screeched before – I couldn't believe my eyes – she locked Her own jaws around the rope bone and shook her head from side to side. Letting out a mock growl at the same time. Dog flattened its ears and slid to the floor while She dropped the bone from her mouth with a grunt. Which didn't stop Her from going back into the toy box and whipping out a dirty yellow tennis ball, shoving it towards Dog's snout. "*ALL* dogs love these!" She said this with slightly gritted teeth, emphasising the word "all" with saucer eyes. All dogs except Dog. The Chow didn't give it a sniff.

She jerked Dog back up by its collar into a sitting position facing Her. "Okay, let's try a chewable bone," this said with a cheery edge. During which She withdrew a small white bone from the toy box and knelt down closer to Dog who immediately looked away. "I *know* you like these, doggy," Her edge was jagged. "Go fetch this one and you can chew it to hell." Dog continued to ignore Her, focusing instead on some invisible bug on the wallpaper.

Undeterred, She threw the bone down the hallway. It landed opposite me. "GO FETCH THAT BONE!" By this time She was barking the command with a gusto bordering on strident. Dog did finally stir itself and began plodding very slowly forward stopping every one or two paces for a sniff at the carpet or skirting board.

"Good doggy, that's a good girl," She'd hoisted herself up from her kneeling position to yell encouragement at Dog's bottom. Dog upped its pace.

"That's it, fetch the bone, that's a clever girl!" She was panting with great expectations.

Suddenly Dog bolted, but not in a rush to retrieve the bone. It flew past me, making a sharp turn to my left towards the office. I lost sight of It but saw Her legs run past my nose shouting, "Come back here you wicked little...."

In that moment I fully expected a Dawgsbody but instead She let out a truly deafening, "Oh, shit, shit, double triple shit, come OUT from behind that desk this minute, do you hear me?"

Dog's return to Obedience School was postponed.

Thursday, 11th September: *Unexpected booty*

PRRR! PRRR! PRRR! Unexpected booty has come cat's way in the form of Good Doggy Fish Cake because of Dog's flagrant disobedience and associated mayhem in the office two days ago. Dog is once again – Prrr! Prrr! Prrr! -- in Her bad books. She is more appreciative than ever of cat's civilised deportment. Hence, She is giving *cat* fish cake (which is a savoury combination of tuna, eggs and garlic) until Dog "pulls up its bootstraps."

Sunday, 14th September: *"Significant breakthrough"*

She has achieved a "significant breakthrough" with Dog after taking advice from Fat Fiona, or so She believes. Fatty suggests that stubborn and resistant Chows can be viewed as master criminals; therefore, their "superior intellects" require more sophisticated approaches to rehabilitation (i.e. training strategies in Dog's case) than do more common lawbreaking breeds.

This afternoon, She tried such an approach called "Hide and Seek the Treat." Dog was encouraged to sit in the hallway while She ran into the lounge to plant a small piece of Good Doggy Fish Cake somewhere within Dog's reach, following which She released Dog to find it. I have to say, once Dog realised what was on offer, It did in fact SIT and STAY patiently every time until She commanded It to "fetch the treat." At which point there was no turning Dog back from its mission.

I watched the exercise from the kitchen window sill. It never took Dog more than seconds to sniff out the succulent titbit and return to Her in the hallway for another go. She is ecstatic. Full of self-congratulation about having identified "the conditions required to facilitate Dog's obedience," which I know She'll claim are infinitely more complex than for canines of purely average intelligence. Nix to *Pooch Perfect*'s comments about Chows!

Monday, 15th September: *A masterless dog?*

Prrr! Finally, She's shut her gob and gone to sleep. About time, too. When *will* She stop going on about Dog? Listening to Her tonight is the cross I had to bear for frequenting my new igloo as Her reward for giving me fish cake (prematurely it now appears). She took my presence as a chance to repeat what I would have called so much "unadulterated bovine excreta" about training Dog.

"You know what Soot?" She began, in a decidedly reflective mood prompting her to reach out and pat me. "Fi says Chows do not attempt to please their masters because in their minds they are masterless!" She withdrew her hand and I heard her sit up against the bedstead. My whiskers fell as I braced myself for a long night. "In other words, Puss, such dogs feel no need to comply with established rules because they make their own."

I wasn't sure where this was leading but the concept of a "masterless" dog intrigued so I cocked an ear and raised my chin to the edge of the igloo. She plumped up her pillows and droned on, "Basically, Chows could be said to resemble hardened criminals of the highly intelligent kind." She paused after that statement, as if waiting for me to comment, and when I didn't carried on, "... implying that when educating them to behave acceptably, we should accord them the dignity and respect they think they deserve, even if they don't. Plus..." Her arms folded across her chest at this stage, "we should provide them with very strong incentives for obeying the rules. What do you think of that, Puss?" She looked in my direction and read my silence as tacit agreement with her drivel which she summed up by saying, "Tomorrow's another day, Pussycat, and we shall persist with our more intellectual approach to training doggy. After all, Hide & Seek's working, isn't it!"

I had absolutely nothing to say. Fatty's the criminal psychologist. I can only surmise that my days of Good Doggy Fish Cake are numbered. Even though the notion of "a masterless dog" does makes me think, especially about the implications of such a dog for Her as opposed to me. At least the mention of "we" in relation to Dog's training is a good sign – A.S. Cat is recovering his household position. Then again, Dog does have Her jumping through hoops.

Tuesday, 16th September: *A sucky American puppet*

Good or bad news to report, depending on one's perspective. Her new "intellectual approach" to Dog's training (bribing It with fish cake as well as Cumberland sausage) seems to be working. Tonight at Obedience School It was extolled as having "wowed" everyone. She couldn't stop talking about Dog's *Pooch Perfect* performance of SITs, STAYs and DOWNs after returning home. Neither could She stop fawning over It in the kitchen after scooping me up out of the hammock and forcing me to join their victory celebration during which Dog scoffed down even more fish cake.

"Oh, doggy, you are SO gorgeous," She syrup-dripped over the Chow's head. She was standing near the counter boiling a kettle for Her evening coffee. Couldn't restrain herself from giving Dog a scratch behind the ears before kneeling down to hug It. Interesting -- Dog stayed frozen to the spot. Unlike 99.9% of other canines I've seen in similar human encounters, It did not tail wag with escalating speed. Quite the reverse, Dog's tail wilted and unravelled behind its bum. Which response completely escaped Her notice as she squeezed the Chow ever tighter. To an objective eye it was another case of unrequited love. Only this time, it was Hers for Dog and not Dog's for me.

"Does doggy want more fish cake?" She purred an enquiry, releasing Dog from the hug to sit back and gaze into Its assuredly beady and conniving slanty eyes.

Its ears perked up and the sagging tail rolled back up into what was indisputably *contrived wagging*. In front of which She dissembled into a smarmy, very sucky American puppet. "Of course you can have more fishy cakees after all the hard work you've done tonight," She required no further incentive to get up and fetch Dog more special treats.

As I mull over Dog's performance in the kitchen, I realise -- despite Its youth, the Chow has a disturbingly old and manipulative head on its stilted little gait. And She doesn't see it.

Thursday, 18th September: *Vicarious thrill of savagery*
Am continuing to lie low to avoid a chance meeting with Petronella. I'm not overjoyed about waiting for my limp to disappear but at least I'm close to jumping on and off the kitchen counter without assistance. Plus, my days of being housebound enable me to take the full measure of Dog.

Take what I learned today about Dog's behaviour during its walk on a nearby golf course at lunchtime. I heard all about it when She rang her mother this evening to extol Dog's "fearless response to a hulk of a Rottweiler" whom She insisted had been trained as an attack dog (which claim I'm sure was manufactured for dramatic effect). The golf club shall remain unnamed but it is noted for bursting with solicitors, accountants and other presumed Very Important People who wouldn't

countenance the potentially hazardous liability of a rapacious Rottweiler on their fairways, let alone their greens.

She says "the whacking great Rottweiler" called Nero
tried mounting Dog three times along the public footpath
between the 8th and 9th holes and, told her mother with
undisguised relish, Dog "gave no quarter." The Chow at
six months only came up to the rotter's kneecaps, yet
thought nothing of baring Its teeth and ferociously growling
the "would be rapist" into a hasty retreat. On top of which
Dog jumped up and bit its would-be assailant's ear, to
leave it in no doubt about who was boss, I'd wager.

While overflowing with pride, She admitted to being
terrified the dog's male owner would sue. Luckily, he just
laughed and said, "I love your dog, mine's a wimp!" Which
She figured was because he was a 30-something sales
type more comfortable with aggressive women than the
average retired 55+ club member.

I draw two conclusions from this incident: first, She has
unconsciously identified the Rottweiler with the Lying
Hound and, through Dog, has had the vicarious thrill of
savaging it; second, I must ensure Dog's future attempts at
dominance are suitably channelled and used to A.S. Cat's
advantage.

Saturday, 20th September: *Dog of war*

Major catastrophe - Dog has a limp! Minor catastrophe -
She is back on Valium! (She first took Valium after the
Lying Hound exited but stopped once I started going to
bed with Her.) Both catastrophes are due to Dog's
disruption of Army war games on the military training

ground where they went for walkies this morning. Dog fell into a trench and injured itself, then went barking through a tripwire in a forested area setting off an explosion which prompted "swarms of cadets to pour out of fox holes in search of enemy," She told me afterwards. The rest is far too tedious to recount, except that Dog has now gained Her sympathy vote, which does not suit me at all.

Monday, 29th September: *Not a brood bear*

The tables have turned. I am back to my old self while Dog limps noticeably after badly spraining its right front leg. It's gone to the vet three times since its escapade on the training ground. No broken bones but x-rays show Dog suffers from osteoarthritis of the right elbow ("Too much inbreeding" says the vet), which might have gone undiscovered if Dog hadn't injured itself.

She is "utterly gutted" at the thought of having an over-bred, now over-priced, physically imperfect pooch. Some of her dog-walking acquaintances advise Her to sue. She's told Fat Fiona legal action won't rid Dog of the problem plus She quotes her English grandfather as saying, "Never go to court, the Law's an ass."

On top of this physical calamity Dog has also begun suffering from "female problems" i.e. It's now "in heat" for the first time. The Chow mopes about panting in the crate with collapsed ears on top of a poor-little-me look. It has no appetite and won't even look at a dental rask chew. It smells funny, too. The odor doesn't tickle my whiskers but will supposedly make male dogs drool.

Most telling, Dog isn't running down the hallway to roust me out of my hammock every chance It gets. All of which engenders Her sympathies when She's not in a state of acute anxiety at the "gaggle of foaming-at-the-mouth males wanting to get their legs over" Dog during walkies. "I cannot possibly entertain the prospect of puppies!" She adamantly tells everyone who asks about Dog's health.

I think Her fear and trepidation about protecting Dog's virginity is overblown. It's no sex-bomb on paws. Seems totally disinterested in male dogs, preferring to chew them into submission than mate with them to produce puppies e.g. the hapless Nero. Dog's more of a killer queen than a brood bear.

Nevertheless, Dog's got even more of Her sympathy votes now. On the plus side today, I took a crack at the brick wall running alongside part of our back garden and purr purr purr, I jumped onto the top of it in a single leap.

Petronella, here I come!

108

October: The Enemy Within

<u>Wednesday, 1st October</u>: *Major gains wiped out*

Weather: Indian summer coming to an end

Hunting prospects: uncertain despite intensive nut-and-acorn burial activity by the Stinking Squirrel

Food: high standards of summer slipping; receipt of fish cake short lived

Accommodation: 4-star down to 2-star i.e. two rest areas demolished due to improved health (pillows gone from lounge sofa and kitchen counter); hammock needs a wash

Entertainment: less than award-winning with indefinite suspension of Obedience School although am well enough to creep along neighbours' walls to watch septuagenarian tortoise Sid humping hard-case Cynthia before dirty old turtle's winter hibernation

Dog's behaviour: capitalising on injured right leg, osteoarthritis and Her sympathies

Her training: stalled; Dog's "severely debilitated condition" has taken Her eye off cat's ball; must reel Her back in as a matter of urgency (Tall order)

Gurr-ow! It is cold although cloudless so that the sun has energised me sufficiently to leap up onto the roof of a neighbour's carport where I can stretch out to enjoy its steady rays in peace. My body feels like the fine physical specimen it was pre-Dog. Yet I am in a depressed mental state, having realised – the past weeks' gains over Dog

109

have been wiped out by the Act-of-God trench-warfare mishap on the Army training ground coupled with Its "female problems." She is paying excessive attention to It which severely undermines my efforts to re-establish cat's power base in the household. While Dog is poorly, my only consolation is the prospect of rubbing noses with Petronella, assuming Posh Puss will give a much older man more than a whisker twitch.

Saturday, 4th October: *The stench of final betrayal*

A rotten stinking fish of a day. She has announced, Dog's banishment to the crate will end. I should have instantly recognised the underlying squirrelousness of Her magnanimous forking out of sardines at breakfast this morning. As I hovered over the salty sea creatures in my bowl on the floor, She delivered my sentence to a life of Dog unrestrained. "So glad you're enjoying the sardines, Soot," She said all bright and breezy from atop a barstool. I was nosing my head around the oily fare. "You're so much better, catkin, aren't you!" I replied, naively in retrospect, by crunching down on a sardine head.

"The vet can't believe you're no longer limping, and to think he wanted to put you under the knife." Her self-satisfied tone at the avoidance of surgical expenditure on me was irritating. "I'm so glad I said 'no' to that, Puss, aren't you?" She leaned down to slide her fingers down my back to the base of my tail, which wafted up into the vertical position. "And isn't it Sod's Law? You're better and doggy's in a dither." At mention of Dog my whiskers started twitching; I sensed something rancid-smelling swimming in the fish barrel of Her words.

"Fact is, Pussycat, Tamba's grown up. Been fully house-trained for months, wouldn't dream of soiling her bedspace." She was all smarm. "Except for that one time in the summer." She twittered on as I crunched through the fragile spine of another sardine, smugly recalling my long and lingering wee in Dog's crate. "Actually, She paused here, "doggy hates being dirty, she's quite catlike in that respect. Loves her freedom, too."

I stopped crunching. A sardine tail protruded from my mouth as I imagined a stinking fish rising to the surface.

"In short, Sooty, it's time our Chow Chow was set free. She's earned the right, Puss, and poor doggy, *she's* the one limping now. She needs lots of TLC, from both of us."

I spat the sardine tail back into the bowl and raised my head. She didn't look at me, too busy tidying up the counter, or too guilty to meet my eyes.

"So, Puss, we're getting rid of that nasty old crate," pausing to discharge the final bombshell, "...on Monday. I've sold it to the vet."

Her words shot me back to that first Day of Infamy when Dog raced through our front door as if It owned my place. To the time It chased my squirrel and brought about cat's fall. The dive bombings on my terrace and to all Its other nefarious actions made bearable by the knowledge It would always go back into the crate.

The stench of Her final betrayal flared up in my nostrils like the most stinking of stinking fish. My appetite dissolved and I meowed loudly as I turned my back on the bowl.

"Puss, you haven't finished brekkies," She carped. That was my signal to slide through the cat flap and leave Her to reflect upon the half-eaten sardines.

Chickens are home to roost – my reprieve from the full impact of Dog's arrival is over. The real battle is beginning.

Monday, 6th October: *No celebration of liberty*

The de-crating of Dog was carried out late this afternoon when I was in my hammock. I accept -- when confronted by humans, we cats have only two choices: change or die. Grrr-ow! I refuse to die because of an overheated pooch imperfect.

In liberating Dog, She acted with what I can only describe as the beneficence of an enlightened despot: pulled open the crate's wire mesh door with a flourish of arm movements and loudly proclaimed Dog free. "C'mon, Tamba Ching, out you come. It's Independence Day!"

Dog, who'd been lying listlessly there for hours, raised its head to look at Her and plonked it back down.

"Oh dear, another bad day?" She crawled into the cage and stroked the listless Chow's bear-like nose. "All right, doggy, come out in your own time." She backed out, somewhat deflated by Dog's indifference and, absurdly, looked over at me for commiseration. "There's no way we're going through *this* a second time." Her voice vibrated a hard, dispassionate crackle and I wondered how She intended to thwart Mother Nature's plan for Dog's passage into womanhood.

"Let her go through one season, the vet told me, Puss." She shook her head before returning her gaze to Dog who'd closed its eyes. "Well, this is it -- never again!" She squared her shoulders and marched out of the room.

After She'd disappeared, Dog got up very slowly, only to collapse back onto its bum, ears flat and looking miserable. (I note, Dog never does anything immediately upon command unless certain types of treats are on offer. Otherwise, if It responds at all, it's always in its own time.) Its reddening coat seemed to have taken on a whitish cast. All in all, It was most morose and bounceless.

A few moments passed and It struggled to get back up. Once on all fours, Dog limped through the crate door and out of Her office, surprisingly unenthusiastic about its newly awarded freedom. After making Its way ponderously into the hallway, It lay down and closed its eyes. There was no raucous celebration of liberty.

As I watched Dog in uncomfortable repose, I almost but not quite felt sorry for It.

Tuesday, 7th October: *The bedroom invasion*

Grrr-ow! It is a damp dark morning and I have just returned from spending the night at Mad Larissa's. I will not make Her feel better by reappearing for breakfast. Absolutely not! I shall remain under the conifer and whip its trunk with my tail. For I am spitting slugs at the fact Dog's taken removal of Its crate as an admission ticket into MY bedroom. The new sleeping arrangements are intolerable! And to think I almost felt sorry for It yesterday!

Last night She allowed It to bed down with us (thinks It's "in shock" from losing the crate and being "in season" for the first time). Moreover, She did so after assuring me earlier that Dog would not be sleeping in Her bedroom but in the office on Its "brand new horribly expensive but specially-designed-for-dogs-of-distinction overstuffed puffball bed bought on the internet for an absolutely ridiculous price, Pussycat!!!"

TRIPLE GRRR-OW! Her proclamation was nothing more than "unadulterated unexpurgated canine excreta," to borrow squirrelous policewoman's favourite phrase. She consistently failed to get the Chow to lie down on the new puffball bed until she laid a trail of Good Doggy Fish Cake chunks from the hallway carpet under my hammock into her office, ending on the made-to-order doggy duvet. Only then did Dog condescend to semi-install itself on a corner of the duvet. She cuddled It rigid in gratitude wearing her elephant-print silk pyjamas and new trunk slippers. I retired to the igloo during this disgraceful display, making sure to give It my most superior upstairs-downstairs look as I sauntered off towards the bedroom.

A few minutes later She came in, half closing the door behind her. Quickly settled down between the sheets and turned off the light. Typically She couldn't resist some noisy blackbird chatter about Dog's having taken to the new duvet. "All she needed was a little encouragement, Puss," She'd said gleefully before wishing me sweet dreams.

After that it was quiet for no more than a mouse squeak before the bedroom door opened to the barely audible pitter patter of disobedient little Chow feet. "Doggy, is that you?" She chirped up. Inane question! I heard It paw the side of the bed, sniffing below me. My fur stood on end before I growled a warning.

"All right, all right, no dog-and-cat fights in here!" She yelped, clicking the bedside light back on. I jumped out of the igloo and crept over to the edge of the bed. Peeping down, I saw the scurrilous Chow reclining on the floor with a fake and forlorn, little-girldog-lost expression on every limb.

"Sorry, doggy, you've got to go back to your own room," She said but without seeing Dog's fuzzy face half buried between its rounded paws, never mind its black eyes glancing upward, studiously soulful, preparing I was absolutely sure to gaze longingly into Hers as She rounded the corner of the bed.

I watched the subterfuge unfold. She looked down at Dog. "Are you lonely all by yourself in that big empty office?" She asked, kneeling down to fondle the abandoned pupsydoodle. A tall stick of elephant-printed butter melted before my eyes. Dog turned Its head to one side and rubbed one fat paw along its muzzle. The elephant butter dripped to the carpet. "Poor doggy, you *have* had a bad time lately, haven't you." I was flapping my tail on the bedspread as I watched the squirrelous dogpat endear itself further by rubbing its eye with the same fat paw. "Oh, you little sweetheart," She exclaimed hugging the masterful manipulator whose performance was something out of *Lassie, Come Home.*

She glanced up at me, mewing an entreaty, "Soot, you don't mind if doggy stays with us, do you Puss Puss?" Then got up off the floor to sit down beside me. Dog raised Its head and two crafty eyes latched onto me. She began patting me while I sat like stone.

"Let's give it a try, shall we?" Ignoring my flapping tail, She gave me a hug and got up to leave the room. Dog lay there gazing up at me with one ear cocked. I raised my nose to the ceiling to avoid what was assuredly Its bewhiskered smugness.

Moments later She returned with Dog's new duvet in her arms. "All right then, doggy, I'll put the duvet at the foot of the bed where you can sleep on it." That was cat's signal to stand up and walk out. No way was I going to spend the night in the same room as Dog. Instead, I exercised the one freedom which Dog will never ever have and that is the freedom to stay out all night and explore any nook or cranny of any neighbourhood A Superior Cat chooses.

"Soot, where're you going, Puss?" She meowed dejectedly this time when I leapt off the bed and stalked out of her room. I sensed Dog was aching to follow but wouldn't dare at such a critical juncture of invading my sleeping quarters.

As I made my way out of the house, I decided to visit Mad Larissa again.

Thursday, 9th October: *Puffball beds are out*
Today, I came in from the cold after two nights away from home, incensed by Her surrender of cat's bedroom to Dog. When I squeezed through the cat flap at breakfast time, She was in the kitchen. Overjoyed to see me of course and trying not to scold. She hates not knowing where I am.

116

Always threatens to notify the Police, vet, Cat's Protection League and anyone else She can think of about my missing person if one of my prowls lasts more than two consecutive nights. I pushed Her to the limit.

"Sooty, where the heck have you been?" She whisked me up off the floor to look me over. "I thought you'd been run over or set upon by foxes. Past myself with worry, Pussycat. Please don't stay out all night, it's no longer summer, you know..." and on and on and on until I meowed forcefully which She took as a sign of hunger. At least I got some Good Doggy Fish Cake for my disappearance, probably because *Her* life's been no bed of field mice either.

It appears that Dog has categorically rejected the "overstuffed puffball bed," preferring to sleep wherever It and not She chooses. She has made repeated efforts to bribe It onto the pillowy sleeping mat with Good Doggy Fish Cake. Even resorted to hiding chunks inside the cover to fool the Chow into sleeping on it. Only Dog refuses to bed down on the duvet or in any other designated space. Insists on deciding for itself where to stretch its constantly exfurriating limbs on Her bedroom carpet. After hours of fruitless repositioning of Dog on the duvet, She tried relocating both back in Her office. Failed miserably. Dog didn't bark disagreement, just scratched at the office door until She gave in and let it back into Her boudoir as being the lesser of two evils.

Dog's bullish behaviour caused Her so much aggro ("furring up the carpet everywhere" requiring her to hand brush and comb out its pile daily) that she called the breeder only to be told, buying beds for Chows – whether molded, mattressed or other – is "a total waste of money" as they and only they decide when and where they sleep. Which comes as bitterly disappointing news given the "horrible expensiveness" of the overstuffed puffball bed.

How do I know all this? Because *She* herself blurted it all out to me, not realising such admissions underscore Her absolute foolishness at one, getting a dog; two, getting a Chow; and three, disposing of the crate. At worst She could have stopped at one.

Saturday, 11th October: Dark and sleepless nights

I am steering clear of the Bed Battles, meaning my igloo has been unused since Dog commandeered Her room. She begs for sympathy ("What AM I going to do with her, Soot? She will not stay put..." etc etc ad nauseam); I leave the house. It's Her problem, not mine, and I can see She is having grave reservations about having sold the crate. She should have consulted me first! What concerns me most is – though Dog is still a Mope About (limping, uncomfortable "in heat" thus less in cat's face than normal), even in this depressed state, It is wearing down Her resolve to get the bedroom back in order and my igloo returned to habitable-accommodation status. Dark circles of sleepless nights lie around Her eyes. Plus yesterday afternoon She booked an appointment with a Reflexologist for a foot massage to relieve what She described to the person on the phone as Her "severe stress and strain from caring for an extremely stubborn relative who won't listen to reason about what's best for them."

Sunday, 12th October: *Blockading my cat flap*

Young Rupert spent the afternoon with us. Marigold dropped him off at teatime, refusing to enter a crate-less house. Rupert felt it his duty as godfather to visit Dog in "her hour of need," not that Dog is remotely needy. Its below-par physical health certainly hasn't dulled its determination to win the Battle of the Bedroom. No amount of "persuasive selling" (Her words) will get It to sleep on the puffball bed or in Her office. Hence, last night I slept in my hammock again.

Rupert was as ever pleased to see me although he found it harder to reach me for our usual cuddle. With Dog on the loose, I've taken to higher ground, seeking out pole positions on top of the kitchen counter, hall bookcase, Her office filing cabinets and anywhere else out of Dog's reach. Fortunately, while Dog grows bigger, Its chunky body and stilted legs do not give it much flexibility or springiness. Most heights above Its own full grown will, I hope, remain out of reach, aiding my intention to keep It "below stairs" and in its place.

Rupert arrived with a godfatherly gift of "delicious meaty roll" dog biscuits. I am touched to say – Rupert observed *House Rule No 2* i.e. patting of cat first, who was waiting on the kitchen counter. She used to take a dim view of my forays across the worktops. But after my fall and Dog's assaults, She quite rightly has allowed me to use these spaces without complaint. They provide me with safe viewing platforms and escape from bad behaviour. From the counter next to the back door, I can see down the length of our hallway to the front door and by gazing to the

119

right, into Her lounge while maintaining the option of a swift exit out the cat flap if necessary.

Rupert greeted me companionably, "Hello, Mr Cat." When he stretched up to pat me, I lowered my head so he could. "Auntie says you're all better now, Sooty."

She was taking freshly-baked but slightly burnt-smelling scones out of the oven. "Yes, he does seem fully recovered from his nasty fall." Said this to him before I could purr my own reply.

"Where's my goddoggy?" Rupert asked proprietarily.

"Shut in the office waiting for her godfather," She chirped, quick to add "but don't be upset if Tamba doesn't get up or wag her tail. She's a bit under the weather."

"But I can give her the biscuits, can't I?"

"Of course you can, my Sweetie Pie." Her eyes were on the scones and didn't see Rupert roll his at mine. I'm sure he thinks Her embellishments of people's names as stupid as I do.

Her godson gave me a reassuring pat, "I'll be back, Sooty," and bounced off. Rupert receives full marks for his astute analysis of the household pecking order.

A few minutes later a slightly droopy-shouldered Rupert returned with Dog padding aimlessly behind. "Auntie, doggy's *really* miserable," he said not as disappointed as he might have been had he not been forewarned. "She didn't touch the biscuits."

"Tamba will when she's better." She smiled encouragingly at Rupert as she picked up a tea tray. "Let's go have tea now, leave doggy here with Sooty." And shepherded Rupert into the lounge. Despite the smell of

120

freshly-baked scones, Dog made no move to follow. Dog had other intentions. It got up and plodded over to the back door and to my utter consternation and disgust lay down and thrust Its fuzzy big head through MY cat flap! A hideous act! Made my fur stand on end before I unleashed a furious growl.

"Sooty, what is it?" I saw Her look up from the sofa where she'd been sitting with Rupert. My tail was doing a semi-circular flap on the kitchen counter so outraged was I at sight of the desecration beneath.

"Surely you don't want any scones, Puss?" She chortled. As usual, totally misread the situation. I was crouched on the side of the kitchen counter peering down at Dog. The wicked godmother got up and walked towards me, Her eyes following mine to the floor.

"Doggy, what on earth…?" She giggled. I couldn't make out the muted, intermittent shushing sound from the furry mass below. She knelt down beside the headless body of Dog and called out softly in the direction of the lounge. "Rupy, Rupy, come here, darling, you must see this. I think doggy's got her head stuck!"

Rupert rushed in to witness the latest of Dog's transgressions, the blockading of my exit route out of the asylum. Adding insult to injury, Dog was snoring Its beastly head off!

Saturday, 18th October: *A disturbing trend*

Dog's blockade of my cat flap is developing into an extremely disturbing trend. Since Rupert's visit (ending in raucous laughter over Dog's antics which are nothing short of a low blow to my independence to come and go as and when I please which I have *always* done until the villainous beast darkened my door) the Chow has stuck its bulbous head through my flap no fewer than 22 times. I have been closely monitoring these attacks on my free passage out into the garden, from the kitchen counter. More worrying, the frequency with which Dog abuses my cat flap daily has been rising in geometric proportion. Worse yet, at times the Chow keeps Its lion-like head in the plug-hole position for as long as it would take me to make a round-trip visit to Petronella's with a sight-seeing tour of Mad Larissa's on the way back.

She finds this "idiosyncratic behaviour" highly comical ("Would you believe, my little Chow loves to snooze with her head out the cat flap? Ha, ha, ha" and all that...). I am beyond grrr-ows when I see It sneaking towards my flap to shove its over-sized cerebellum through the pathway to my garden. Is there no end to Its invasiveness? More and more I realise, I may have to scout out alternative roofs over my head to ensure my movements are not haphazardly restricted.

Tuesday, 21st October: *Who's been in MY bed?*

It is late afternoon, getting darker by the minute. A chill wind's cutting through my fur as I hunch down on the wall alongside the terrace. My tail smacks the bricks in disgust; I cannot stomach going back into the house now that She and the flap buster have returned even though I've been gone for another two days, searching for greener pastures in the face of Dog's persistent attempts to take over my flap and control my movements.

I arrived back this morning, found the house strangely quiet. No sign of Her or Dog anywhere. So I went walkabout to fully assess the condition of my accommodation following Her crate disposal and Dog's free run of my house since. What did I find???

My kitchen

- C-A-T embossed food bowl upside down on the floor
- My water bowl empty
- A shiny new bigger-than-mine bowl with chicken-flavoured nuggets in it (helped myself although I almost cracked my teeth on them)
- Old willow-pattern bowl half full of water (drained it)

My hallway

- My sheepskin hammock with half-chewed strip of dental rask lying in it (no doubt tossed in by Dog)
- Dog's dish brush, totally legless

My office

- Dirty pawprints on the carpet
- No overstuffed puffball bed

My bedroom

- No overstuffed puffball bed
- A stingray-shaped scrap of carpet fanning out across almost one third of total floor space of bedroom (Her caving-in solution to Dog's puffball bed rejection)
- My igloo NOT on Her bed but stuffed into a shelf above her bedside table AND, upon closer examination by me jumping up onto the table, I noted that "someone" (no

need to ask WHO!!!) has been busy chewing the border around my igloo bed !!

The sight of my violated bed sent my tail into a GRRR-OW MAXIMUS swishing but I didn't have the satisfaction of even one 360-degree revolution! I heard a key turn in the front door signalling return of the wicked godmother and Her squirrelous goddoggy. My tail stopped swishing instantly. I wanted squirrelous godwomen to find A.S. Cat sitting on the bed like a deadly cobra ready to strike.

It didn't take long for Dog to sniff me out. Seconds after their return, I saw a woolly head thrust itself around Her half-closed bedroom door. The Chow was straining at the leash, just like old times. Its rabid panting, violent nose twitching and pointy ear fluttering told me, limp or no limp, Dog was out of heat and ready to go back into a full-court oppress. Our eyes locked and Dog knew that I knew It was guilty of vandalising my bed. I sat like an unexploded bomb ticking away, *The British Army is fish cake compared to me, dogbat!*

Thursday, 23rd October: *It's a War Zone out there!*
Am back home, shivering on the terrace, after more days and nights out on the prowl in protest of Dog's attack on my igloo bed. How many more disappearances will it take for Her to get the message? She hasn't so far, judging from her no less than snide queries about my absence: "Pussycat, you're not *still* going out on the prowl for gorgeous moggies, are you?"

124

The problem is -- journeying into the cold to look for other places to hang my head is not the answer either. I've come to realise – it's a War Zone out there, too!   The weather's no longer conducive to pleasant strolls.   Too damp in the late evening and too frosty in the early morning to camp out underneath conifers the whole time.

Last night was particularly awful. I was on the move on and off all night long. Started under the conifer near the terrace but when it began to rain, it got so damp I trotted over to Mad Larissa's; the late Trotsi's cat flap was boarded up! I tried the flat roof of our neighbour's car port, part of which is shielded by low-hanging branches of a feathery pine tree. The rain had stopped by the time I'd jumped up and settled down on its slightly gritty roof. But the wind picked up and my tail kept flapping.   I wasn't about to fight my tail all night!

I found a garden shed with its door open. A bit risky, strange sheds. One never knows what's lurking inside. As I couldn't catch a whiff of anything overtly off putting, I went in and settled down on a sack of what smelled like fertiliser. At least it was dry and reasonably comfy. As I was nodding off, a measly hedgehog appeared in the doorway. Probably on a snail or slug sweep after the rain. My fur stood on end, he popped his quills and I decided, best take a flying leap over and out of there. Didn't fancy spending the night with that flea-ridden forager!

By then I was so tired and downcast I settled for the "no-man's land" of a deserted dog kennel in a garden on another road. Didn't think another cat would be in it although rats crossed my mind so I crept slowly through the doorway. It was deathly quiet. No wonder. The small wooden hut stank of a faint mix of mould and fetid pools of water mixed with dog. Too tired to care, I spent what was left of the night there until in the light of dawn, a fox cub poked its head in. I jerked upward, spat at it. The cub turned tail and skittered out. So did I. Had no desire to rub noses with its elder. A dreadful night, all tolled.

Even wandering the streets in daytime was hazardous. I've been so preoccupied with Dog and recovering from my fall that I've failed to notice how the neighbourhood's changed. It's full of cats I've never seen before, different breeds from those I used to know.

Take the ones I saw yesterday afternoon after jumping onto the stone wall on the other side of our street for a nap. I figured the wall, belonging to a cat-less house, would be a sun trap, a safe haven from which to observe the street below. Grrr-ow! I couldn't *believe* what went on. First, a screeching ball of red-and-black fur with two tails twitching out of it tumbled out of the bushes onto the pavement a few yards away. An American Wirehair scrapping with a Bombay Black like two stupid dogs fighting over a bitch in heat. They were a revolving furore until an old woman with a stern expression came out from behind a hedge and threw a pan of water over the yobs. "Get out of here, or I'll set the dog on you!" The chastised combatants sped off in opposite directions.

Not long afterwards I noticed a corpulent but muscular grey-and-white striped tabby crouched beneath a shrub in front of a house beyond ours. He was pawing at the ground like an angry bull. Before I could blink, he'd leapt across the road to pounce on a Siamese caught completely by surprise. The Siamese dealt him one swift paw swipe, then shot off down the street. The truculent tabby slunk back across the road to lie in wait under another shrub even closer to our house!

All I'd wanted was a cat nap. Instead I had tails from Sodom and Gomorrah before me. Yet, it had been so lovely and warm on the wall, I didn't want to move until the scent of a rude familiar hit my nostrils. It set my tail bristling and swishing to and fro. My ears pricked and furled back as the pupils of my eyes closed into two slits to pierce the gleaming black face of that same Bombay I'd seen thrashing around with the Wirehair. It had leapt up onto the end of my wall to lie there menacingly like an Indian leopard, tail whipping from side to side despite my undisputed right of way.

I didn't wait for the slick-pawed upstart to start playing territorial games. Dashed forward and punched at its jaw with my right paw while waving my tail to the left to keep my balance. The intruder was caught out by my swift and aggressive action and jumped down into the bushes below. I crouched low to watch it flee.

At first I felt the ecstasy of victory at upending a younger challenger. Glowered at its defeat by the dangerous assumption that a 17-year-old neutered tom would run. In seeing the panther-like prowler off, I fantasised about defending my wall against all other trespassers until an agonising truth hit me: I had only climbed up there to enjoy a cat nap, I hadn't had one and now the sun was gone. In that moment I realised, it was no good staying out all night to solve my problems. I would have to return home and confront the enemy within.

Wednesday, 29th October: *A penny has dropped*

A single penny has dropped. She has recognised that Dog's interference with my cat flap seriously restricts my freedom. Today, She erected a barrier of sorts to halt Its blockading tactics. This consists of lining up a rubbish bin and barstool in front of the back door right before bedtime and at various other times of day. There is enough space for me to crawl past the left side of this barrier and out the cat flap. Dog is prevented from plugging it with Its furry snout.

As ever a flea has already got stuck in the ointment: Dog has started lying down in front of the bin and barstool. Happily, some of Her re-training has taken hold; She pulled Dog up and away from this position three times today. A small victory and one which convinces me I cannot afford to lose control of the low ground, meaning the probability of more direct physical confrontation and paw-to-paw combat grows daily.

As an aside She has announced that Her American niece Magda will arrive the day after tomorrow for "a flying visit on her way to Europe." She is all excited because She wants Magda, who already knows me, to meet Dog and thinks it might be fun to "do Halloween." I don't really know what Halloween is except I've heard it's something to do with opening one's door to beggars.

<u>Friday, 31st October:</u>   *Happy Halloween* !!!

Imitation is *not* the sincerest form of flattery. Today proves it. I found out exactly what She meant by "doing Halloween." And it wasn't fun or funny. I don't blame Magda. I'm sure she only went along with the mad scheme to humour her eccentric aunt. The guilt for my dishonour is Hers and Hers alone.

She'd been on a slippery slope with me since breakfast when she said Magda would only be with us for one night and that Dog and I were to be "on our good behaviour" and I should not "go out on the razzle" this evening.

I was appalled She should lecture me thus, treating me as if I were coupled with Dog. Dog is an uneducated, ignorant pup. I am A Superior Cat. It is unconscionable She should address *me* as "you two."

After She left to walk Dog, I disappeared through the cat flap with every intention of "going out on the razzle" for two more nights, no matter how cold or wet it got. Even if I had to sleep in that horrid dog kennel a second time. Magda would have to do without me this visit. But my carefully-laid plan was blown apart by a Halloween happening so insidious and insulting, it's hard to repeat.

I spent most of the raw grey of today strolling around the garden, lying low under the conifers or hiding in the shrubs as long as Dog wasn't around. Whenever I heard the back door open, I'd pop over the nearest wall or fence. At one point I was at the bottom of the garden hoping to find the Stinking Squirrel nut gathering when She and Magda came out onto the terrace with Dog. My cover was almost blown when It rushed down the steps. Only just managed to leap the fence into our neighbour's garden. Being out on the razzle was already great fun, I thought. How wrong I was.

When darkness fell, evil that women do arose in monstrous spectres of cats defiled. I witnessed effects of the witchery at close range although at first I couldn't actually see the sorcerers. From the top of our wall I watched little children dressed as ghosts, goblins and garden gnomes chattering away, laughing as they walked hand in hand with their elders down our drive. I heard them knock on the front door. A pause, silence and then screaming and crying.

The next thing I saw was the tiny ones being huddled quickly back up our drive and out onto the street. Parents were trying to comfort the children saying things like, "It's only make believe. They're not real monsters. Dressed up for Halloween is all."

That's when I realised, She was "doing Halloween." Only the visitors weren't beggars but neighbourhood children and it was debatable how much *fun* they were having. I jumped down from the wall and crept unseen through the space between the car and fence along the drive. After I'd slunk past the boot of the car, I leapt across the drive and into the front garden so I could crawl through its evergreen shrubs back towards our entrance to see for myself the origin of the children's distress.

Light from our porch cut through the bushes. As I slithered underneath the greenery, I heard a merry duo of Her and Magda call out "Happy Halloween" as the last of some tearful little folk disappeared into the darkness. I reached the dwarf conifer at the edge of the garden, and peeped around it for a clear view.

Even before I could logically take in the sight before me, my tail skyrocketed upwards and my back arched to spit out a GRRR-OW MAXIMUS before I could stop it. For there rising up before my scandalised eyes, in shameless impersonation of my species, were Her and Magda dressed up as two horribly huge black cats with pointy ears, whiskers and long tails drooping practically to the ground. Only She was wearing a white bib, furry looking white gloves and white kneesocks.

I was in shock and awe as I looked down at my own white paws, and the last thing I heard before hurtling myself back through the shrubbery to the sanity of an abandoned dog kennel was Her cry of entreaty, "Pussycat, Pussycat, it's only me!"

November: GRRR-OW! Scumbugs!

Saturday, 1st November: *Digging my claws in*

Some Happy Halloween! More like the night from hell in a damp scurvy dog kennel. At least I didn't have to share my bed space with another nocturnal wanderer although I could have done without all the pigeon feathers and stench of mutilation. I wonder if foxes use the malodorous hutch as a slaughter house. Wish they'd have a go at Dog.

By the time I returned home late this morning, Magda had left. The alleged owner was fractious, having serious difficulty removing her cat whiskers. Or perhaps she was chastened by memories of screaming children. Before going back into the house, I jumped onto the brick wall at the end of the drive to survey the garden. Grrr-ow! Dog was lying at the bottom gazing up at the conifer where the Stinking Squirrel hangs out.

It's inescapable. I will have to dig my claws in to get the household back in order. The disruptive Chow has accelerated its deterioration. The weeks ahead will not be easy.

Weather: dewy nights herald unpleasant slugfests on my terrace until serious frosts decimate the slimy gastropods. Would that Dog would eat a poisoned one!

Hunting prospects: no cause for optimism about garden booty with Dog roaming about at will

Food: fair at best; few special treats on offer

Accommodation: 2-star declining to no-star after Dog's chewing of igloo bed, blockading of cat flap and reprehensible state of unwashed, dilapidating-fast sheepskin hammock.

Entertainment: paws down if She indulges in further objectionable impersonations of my cathood

Dog's behaviour: overbearing, overrated, underhanded

Her training: gone off the rails, now crashed and burning; major rethink about clawback of cat's position is of highest priority

Monday, 3rd November: Roguishly normal

Miserable cold wet day. Hated going outside to wee and poo. Had to, though, when Dog wasn't in the way. My litter tray was taken away after Dog started nosing my poo during my recovery from the fall. Now when It jams my cat flap and I have to wee, my life's a nightmare! She's become lax about erecting the barrier and I can't go out without a fight. On the flip side, Dog's obsession with my flap keeps It occupied. It spent most of this morning with Its snout hanging out. Giving me the freedom to alternate between sleeping in the hammock and curling up in my roughly-sewn-up-crookedly-by-Her igloo bed.

I am not enamoured about returning to the bedroom to sleep with Dog under foot but there are practical considerations. Dog is almost tall enough to poke its nose right down into my hammock. Her bed is quite high off the ground. With Its overbred, inflexible knee joints, Dog is disinterested in jumping onto it. The bed remains a place for A.S. Cat to nap undisturbed. But for how long? This afternoon the vet pronounced Dog sufficiently recovered from Its run-in with the Army to "resume normal activity." If you ask me, the vet's very slow on the uptake; Dog's been roguishly "normal" for weeks! The question is – how much more "normal" will It become?

Tuesday, 4th November: *"Back to square one"*

This evening Dog re-started Level 1 of *Pooch Perfect's* general obedience training for, is it the third or fourth time??? I don't know if it makes me pleased or displeased to record – Dog's performance tonight was "pitiful." Or so She told Fat Fiona a little while ago. I was in my igloo when She rang Fatty from the bedroom. No idea where Dog is.

Fatty was talking loud enough for me to get the gist of their burble about Her being "back to square one" with Dog. It did nothing but "cock Its bum" at Her the whole evening, She claims. Guess She wanted to pour out all Her bugstrations to Fatty who, I inferred, asked Her leading questions like:

- Did you feed Dog before going? ("Of course not!" -- Her reply sounded distinctly waspish.)
- What treats did you use? (Gravy bone dog biscuits)
- What treats did you use last time? (Bits of Good Doggy Fish Cake)

After the Good Doggy Fish Cake mention, She got a bit shirty judging by the way she popped off the bed like a shrieking parrot flying the coop. I think She was having a slight disagreement with Fatty over how to "re-motivate"

135

Dog after its training hiatus. The rest of their conversation went something like this:

Her: head shaking, "You mean stick with Fish Cake?"

Fat Fiona: ?

Her: with severely wrinkled brow, "AND Cumberland sausage?"

Fat Fiona: ?

Her: pacing, letting out controlled parrot shriek, "But Chows AREN'T highly intelligent, hardened criminals!"

Fat Fiona: ?

Her: pacing stopped, one hand on waist, other squeezing life out of portable phone, face contorted into two crevasse-ridden brows: "Do you have ANY idea how much these incentives for good behaviour cost?"

I am not overjoyed at the thought of Dog getting fish cake once a week although my tail flaps with alacrity at visions of Her jumping through hoops again!

Wednesday, 5th November: *Flap buster strikes again*

Incredible! Dog's taken out my cat flap AGAIN! Literally! This evening, on Guy Fawkes Night, when the sky above our house lit up like Christmas trees with sounds like gunfire pelting us from every angle. Had I not known about this strange celebration or been a discerning cat, I might have thought the Army was counter attacking Dog. She never expected a re-run of the jet-fighter fiasco from *inside* the house. That's for sure. And now of course there's no crate to straitjacket Its "fireworks dementia."

The debacle started early on, when the road began hotting up with the snap of firecrackers. She was in the office, I in my hammock and Dog was far too animatedly scurrying around the house like a wild rabbit. Until It ran past me into the bathroom and stayed there whimpering. Was It sensing big bangs to come? Are memories of wars lost by the Imperial Chinese rulers of Its Chow ancestors embedded by heredity in Dog's psyche? Perhaps that explains why an ignorant puppy reacts so violently to explosions of commemoration. She can't.

Whatever, Dog's trouble began in the toilet. As soon as She followed after It, I heard Her, "Oh, doggy, it's all right," trying to soothe. "Come on, come out of the corner." Her soothing audibly strained. "No, don't go there!" To which Dog chattered back a few raspy barks. Followed by Her walking a line between Florence Nightingale and General Patton. "Oh no! PLEASE don't tell me you're stuck again!" With Patton winning, "Oh, bitch of a thousand bitches!" Dog by comparison had gone strangely quiet. I asked myself then -- did It feel safe behind a human crapper?

At that point She rushed out of the bathroom. "Sooty, she's trapped behind the loo!" Gritted teeth and wild eyes raised human hands to strangle the air. I calmly rested my chin on the edge of the hammock and regarded Her through half-closed eyes. She lowered her hands and jammed them into her waist. "Right, I'll go call Fi, see if she can pop over to help."

While She was on the phone, I was startled to see Dog speed past me, heading for the kitchen, miraculously self-extracted from jeopardy. I jumped out of the hammock and sprinted after It. As I scampered into the kitchen, I saw It bulldozing the rubbish bin and bar stool fronting my cat flap with such force It toppled the stool and set upon my cat flap with barbarous head thrusts backwards and forwards repeatedly. The door banged against its frame until Dog had squeezed everything but its bottom and curled-up tail through the small hole.

At that moment She swept into the kitchen. "Holy shit!" She screeched, dropping to her knees. She tried to pry Dog out of my violated cat flap while I sat down to supervise near the rubbish bin. But no amount of pulling could de-flap Dog. Its furry body had plugged the flap tight as a wine stopper and all we could see was a woolly bum and two stilted legs silently kicking at air. No squealing, not even a bark accompanied Dog trying to do a runner.

After a few more minutes of futile wrestling with Dog's hind quarters, She let go of them, collapsed exhausted on the floor, Her back against the counter. It too stopped moving. Sadly, there was no blood anywhere.

"What the hell do we do now, Soot?" She brushed one hand through her hair, looking at me forlornly. "Do I call the fire department?" Her furrowed brow quizzed Dog's bottom. "They rescue cats out of trees." She was mumbling to herself more than me. "What about the vet? She could be hurt! Right, I'll call Fi back." She didn't wait for my views, propelled herself up off the floor and down the hallway before I could meow.

Dog's haunches rested on the floor; its tail unrolling down its backside like an inflating paper party whistle. Every so often Its legs twitched. I couldn't hear any panting. Was It in its final death throes, I'd dared hope. Then again, I realised that the fireworks had stopped. More likely, Dog was enjoying sniffing the night air in suspended animation, I thought ruefully.

In the end Fat Fiona came over to anchor the rescue operation from the inside while She climbed out the kitchen window to find Dog "Would you believe it, snoozing, Fi!" When they got the back door open, I could see the rim of my cat flap encircling Its neck for the second time. She cut it off with garden shears. But only after chopping off enough of Dog's fur to make it resemble half a spring lamb, to avoid "ripping pupsydoodle's guts out" and enable them to pull Dog's backside out of the flap by gripping its shoulders.

When Dog was finally freed, It took off like a hare to the bottom of the garden, seemingly none the worse for wear. She and Fatty buckled into heaps on the lounge sofa over drinks. For my part I crouched on the kitchen floor gazing through the empty space that had been my cat flap. It struck me then as it does now: Dog gets demented but when in a real hole, is remarkably cool under pressure. Others might have squealed like pigs, barked in terror or sunk their teeth into helping hands. Not Dog. It remained unflustered, like that first time on the terrace when I nailed Its lip with my claws. The furry flap buster has far too many lives for my liking – and looks even more like a lion.

Friday, 7th November: *Nerves are frayed*

More dog drama. It did not emerge from my cat flap unscathed after all. Today, Dog woke up with another limp (bad elbow leg again). She is demented with worry and rushed it off to the vet who's prescribed Valium twice a day for the next week to calm It down. Plus It needs jabs to heal its osteoarthritic elbow.

Her "nerves are frayed" and She will probably steal some of Dog's tablets when It isn't looking. In addition to which the fireworks continue. Which means we have to listen to Mozart every night until they stop because of something She calls "The Mozart Effect," which in theory reduces stress and induces sleep.

On top of which this afternoon She constructed a cardboard shanty town in Her office i.e. a makeshift crate of sorts using stacked cardboard boxes, large-size rubbish bags rolled out flat on the floor and blankets spread out over top of the boxes, all to "closet doggy for the night and make It feel safe and secure despite all the noise outside."

Why is the Flap Buster such a wuss? Couldn't She have brought home a man dog? Guess a real dog might give me a harder time. Or would he?

If nothing else, I have another new cat flap with a plastic door as transparent as polished glass. From a reclining Sphinx position in the kitchen, I can see right to the bottom of the garden. Highly advantageous. It could enable me to streak out of the kitchen to catch the Stinking Squirrel unawares. Unless the Flap Buster blocks my view for the hundredth time.

Sunday, 9th November: *Never beauty did I see...*

Ah bliss! Never did I true beauty see until today when I rubbed noses with Petronella for the first time. For once

140

Fate conspired in my favour: it was gloriously sunny; the She devils were gone; the house and garden were mine.

I stretched out on my right side across the step immediately below the cat flap. That step catches any sun which rises for most of the day, keeping the bricks warm. From there I can see out across the upper tier of our garden into part of the lower one near the boundary fence at the bottom and beyond, down the sloping terrain into two other gardens running parallel to ours, to the wall where I first saw Petronella when I was still limping.

I realise now, Dog's emerging militarism has kept me so preoccupied I hadn't thought much about the silver tabby until today. Nature must have read my mind. Sweet synchronicity! As my eyes swept the scene below, there she was again -- that cat's meow of a pussycat, ringed in silver and black. Only she wasn't creeping but perched like an Egyptian goddess on the same brick wall, casting her eyes in my direction with consummate self-possession in her stance and an unmistakeable message in that motionless body: *Those who are meant to meet me must make the first move.*

My tail twitched as I rose up on all fours and sat back down on the step to match her disposition. A flock of questions flew across my mind: Should I answer her unspoken summons? How? Scamper down the hill and leap over the fence? Dash like a besotted ferret across our neighbour's lawn and up onto the top of the brick wall to sit beside her? And once there, what? Wrap my tail around her neck and slither it across her luxuriant flanks? Push my head against her cheek in search of a long and languorous nose rub? Or do I stay put? A lizard lounging on a step, blind to the eyes upon it?   Do I remain A Superior Cat demanding the female inferior come to him?

In the next instant a new truth hit me like a flying squirrel landing, thud, on a tree branch. Such questions only arise in the cat-and-mouse games which guide *human* interaction. Yet, the state of human interaction is chaos. They cannot therefore be the right questions.

No, Sooty, I said to myself, *you are above all a cat; follow your instincts, not your head (It may be befuddled by 15 years of living with Her!). Do what cats do: allow your curiosity to take over; get up and move out towards the subject of your fascination with dignity, grace and determination. Let Nature take its course.*

I sat up taller and boldly returned Petronella's stare, imagining her sea green eyes. Her ears pricked, her tail accorded me a lingering twitch. I could feel my nose wrinkling, my whiskers vibrating. The silver tabby sedately lay down and wrapped a luxurious tail around her legs. That was all the encouragement I needed. I jumped down onto the terrace and strode across it with the hauteur of the most magnificent of panthers hunting for a mate.

Monday, 10th November: *Sunny memories*

The chilly rain of today cannot erase the sunny glow of my first encounter with Petronella. She is the rarest of beings: pure as the driven snow, an incomparable rose albeit clawless, which is why Silver Puss's access to the world at large is monumentally restricted. At night her owners lock her cat flap to ensure she doesn't meet with any harm.

142

This is a trial for any cat with nocturnal curiosity; however, they are right. Too many foxes are having a go at us these days.

During the daytime she is likewise sequestered, especially if the weather is brutal. About the only time Puss is allowed to roam free is weekends when her owners are around to keep a watchful eye. They weren't the ones to de-claw her. Do humans like having parts of *their* toes cut off? Activities I take for granted like chasing the Stinking Squirrel, springing up walls, climbing trees, even having a good old stretch are arduous or impossible for angel puss. Thank goodness, Petronella doesn't have a Dog in her life. She couldn't give It a meaningful pawswipe.

Why does any creature, even the two-legged one, rob another of its natural defences unless its own back is against the wall? Petronella really shouldn't be jumping up onto them but she is proud, resilient and uncomplaining.

PRRR! She let slip too, she's been wanting to meet me for weeks. I was unaware that the Bombay Black I'd seen off the stone wall is considered something of a bully who flouts community rules about rights of way and usage of hunting grounds, meeting places and no-man's lands. News travels fast about cats who step outside the law, faster still about cats who put them right. Apparently, I am known as the Bombay Bouncer.

Monday, 17th November: *As if It were behaving*

Another rotten day in my Dog-ridden home. Rainy and cold. The Chow is off Valium, limping less and bothering me more. Almost every time I go into the hammock, It

143

shoves its wet nose over the edge, unless She's nearby. Today, when She was in the lounge, It took its first paw swipe at me there. I clawed its nose. Did It stop? No! It interpreted the action as a game, swiped at me again! Luckily, She came out of the kitchen to go to Her office. Had no idea what Dog was up to but when It saw Her, the devious Chowpat sat down as if it were behaving!

Saturday, 22nd November: *Now, a cat-snuffing corgi!*

Rats! Rumours of a renewed canine influx into our neighbourhood are manifesting as irrefutable fact. Another one of *them* has put its paws on my territory. My doorstep, to be precise. Our neighbours, the Houndslows, have taken on a three-year-old Welsh Corgi with the absurd name of Cowboy Bebop.

She is overjoyed because Dog will have "a built-in playmate." I am far from enthusiastic about having a short-legged foxy-face next to us. I've never personally run into a Corgi before but I've heard about them. A bunch of cattle creepers, with a reputation for being dictatorial and full of themselves at having infiltrated royal ranks of the human order. As if that were an achievement!

This afternoon I caught sight of the interloper after She told me the "great news" of his arrival this morning. The new cow dog was let out into the Houndslow's garden when I happened to be on the terrace. Dog was inside so I made it my business to hop up onto the top of the brick wall running part way down the boundary between the two properties so I could take a look. Not impressed. Bebop reminds me of a low-slung pig with reddish fur and big

144

ears. And I swear I heard Mrs Houndslow tell Her through the garden fence that the dog's a "cat killer."

The thought of a cruddy cat-snuffing Corgi taking up residence on one side of my house with a truculent tabby mugger on the other and Dog cavorting in between is anything but "great news." Far from getting me off the hook, the advent of Cowboy Bebop will likely put me on a seriously sharpened skewer, especially if Mrs Houndslow accepts Her invitation to bring Bebop over for tea! Violation of *House Rule No 4* about not ganging up on cat is a shoe-in unless Dog does a Rottweiler on the beast.

Sunday, 23rd November: *Star-crossed lovers?*

Slings and arrows of canine misfortune have descended not upon my house alone but Petronella's too. Today I strolled down the road to pussycat's domicile which sits at the end. It's very grand with a circular drive and the reported "his and her Mercedes" parked outside. A high brick wall extends from both sides of the house along the rest of the front and behind it to enclose a large garden at the rear. Which means Petronella is walled in when she strays outside. A mild annoyance at worst for a cat with claws; an ongoing challenge for Silver Puss.

When I reached the pavement in front, I slink-ran through a shrub border on the left to a small tree. Some of its branches had grown above the brick wall, my ladder to the top. My heart beat furiously, my whiskers were all a twitch as I scaled its leafy branches to reach one above the wall. From there I leapt down onto the top of it and dashed towards pussycat's back garden.

I turned a corner, looked down onto a well-tended lawn bordered with glossy shrubs. There was a small shed and beside it, a woodpile against one section of the wall but no Petronella. I scurried along until the shed was directly beneath me and jumped down onto its flat roof hoping pussycat would detect my presence from wherever she was. A flap in the back door of the house caught my eye.

As I sat patiently grooming myself in late morning sun, the discordant sounds of yappy barking rudely broke my concentration. I stood up and arched my back. The yapping came closer and I crept very slowly to the edge of the roof to see its source. There below me were two sets of frenetic brown eyes of the West Highland Terrier kind.

My fur went skyward, tail ballooning. I growled deeply which sent the Westies into more frenzied barking and mad rushing back and forth in front of the shed. A distinctly female voice yelled out mildly irritated, "Shush, stop all that racket. Mangle, Wurzel, come here." It belonged to a model-thin but full-breasted blond woman in figure-hugging black leather trousers and ruby red jumper belted tightly at the waist. She wore over-size gardening gloves and carried a rake in one hand although with her high-heeled boots, she appeared better suited for the catwalk.

Being dogs, the aforementioned Mangle and Wurzel took no notice but my fur settled down; the two were all bark and no bite at this level of engagement. I peered down at the mindless minions from the edge of the shed roof. It was rather thrilling watching the peripatetic pooches panting profusely to impossibly propel themselves upwards to pry me off my perch. My tail whipped the air at their clown-like performance until its implications struck home: their presence was Petronella's absence. Where *was* Silver Puss? Who were Mangle and Wurzel anyway? Why were they in her garden?

The dogs barked until the woman threw down her rake and marched over. "That's it, into the house with both of you," she barked louder, grabbing at their collars. After both were in hand, she looked up at me. "Hello there, pussycat, time you went home, isn't it?" She gave me a fleeting smile before frog marching the two Scottish marauders inside the house.

The garden was quiet. I looked around, waited for the woman to return, hoping she might bring Petronella with her. But she didn't. There was no sign of Silver Puss anywhere. Are we fated to become star-crossed lovers?

Tuesday, 25th November: *Sometimes life's a bitch*

Answers to my burning questions about Petronella's precarious situation have come unexpectedly from Her. (She has no idea about my attempted visit.) Lately She has developed knee problems. "Old field hockey injuries," She maintains. More like the after-effects of trying to wrest Dog out of my cat flap. Whichever, She came across Petronella's owner at the doctor's surgery.

Turns out the "30-something" Gillian Fenbinder (She's already nicknamed her "Fender-Bender"!) knackered her knees while chasing Mangle and Wurzel down the road after they bolted in hot pursuit of a "tree rat." (Better not be the Stinking Squirrel!) Fender-Bender made the mistake

Tuesday, 25th November: *Sometimes life's a bitch*

of pursuing the Westies in "exceptionally high-heeled shoes" and fell off them when one heel got caught in a crack in the pavement. She crashed down on both knees causing her such excruciating pain she used her mobile phone to ring her husband to collect her!

The "little terrors" belong to Fender-Bender's parents who're on a six-month cruise. Fender-Bender claims the "rascals" wouldn't dream of actually hurting Petronella but I know her life will be a misery with them around. She can't ever claw them into submission. More to the point, how will *we* ever meet if those two scrub brushes are dogging our every pawstep? Sometimes life's a bitch and always you die.

Friday, 28th November: *Nothing short of a pisser*
Today is a pisser. Raining "cats and dogs," as She would stupidly say. No chance of running round to Petronella's. Putting me in a cantankerous mood, aggravated by Her announcement this morning of "cutbacks in household expenditure" to compensate for her ailing business (my assessment) and "the unanticipated expenses of doggy" (alleged owner's own admission). The cutbacks demand future purchase of "less expensive" cat food i.e. Own Store Label instead of "heavily advertised branded fare" which, She insists, is "always premium priced and a luxury *we* (She daren't say "you, Sooty!") have to do without for the time being."

She also spent all day mouthing off about her newest money-making venture -- registering Dog with *PetStars*, a human agency for merciless exploitation of "garden-variety pets." (She has been constantly telling people, Dog would look "ab fab sitting regally on green velvet to sell Irish whiskey!") Dog (meaning Her), She says, will not be choosy about Its assignments and "stoop to shoot catalogues" although It (again, Her) would prefer work for films or quality magazines. However, She told Fat Fiona, "Under no circumstances will my dog be licking chocolate ice cream off any naked bodies, despite its highly visual and sensual black tongue!"

Per usual She glosses over potential fleas in the ointment, namely how Dog will satisfy *PetStars'* requirements for one, proven levels of dog obedience, and two, tricks "performed on command and repeatedly many times over." The only trick Dog does is getting Her jumping through hoops. Granted It does that repeatedly but never on command.

Sunday, 30th November: *Still raining*

GRRR-OW! Scumbugs! It's still raining. Am not sorry to see the fag end of this month. It's been one bugstration after another: atrocious weather, short days and raucous Westies crowding pussycat's house and preventing us from rubbing noses! Added to which, I feel tired much of the time, even after long naps.

Dog refuses to leave me alone. It must have pushed its slimy snout into my hammock half a dozen times today. Is back to Its old trick of lying in front of my cat flap to block my exit. My only relatively safe haven is the igloo bed but using that means having to listen to all Her problems! Retreating to the tops of bookcases and filing cabinets gets me out of Dog's firing line but these are not comfortable places and the lounge has been off limits (to Dog and thus me) for some time.

My terrace is a battlefield. Seems like every time I go out there to enjoy a bit of sun, Dog's right behind me. I can't even poop without It sniffing my backside! If I give it a pawswipe, It bounces and bats its fuzzy mitts back at me.

Cowboy Bebop, the dog next door, hasn't shown up on our doorstep yet but the Corgi revels in barking every time I walk past him down the top of our fence. Has my once peaceful and quiet life gone forever?

December: The Turning Point

Tuesday, 2nd December: *Rather out of sorts*

Grrr-ow! I am rather out of sorts. Unusually thirsty again. Have been for weeks despite the cold and wet although it's been sunny since yesterday. Am ravenous too, even for Her down-graded cat food. I haven't caught a mouse in ages. Feel too lethargic to bother. I'd sleep all day if the Chow wasn't dogging my every footstep.

I simply must pull myself together. Remember I'm a cat. Getting on perhaps but still amongst the master species who run faster than humans, smell things they can only dream of, jump five times higher than my height (*They* can't!) and detect changes in the environment which people are not remotely capable of perceiving. I must not forget what even the two-legged creatures have admitted, "The smallest feline is a masterpiece."

Weather: drier days forecast may permit daytime jaunts to Petronella's. Prrr! Prrr! Prrr!

Hunting prospects: declining rapidly in face of own disinterest and competition from Dog and new mutt louts

Food: edible just; no prospect of fish cake due to cost-savings programme (She's ignoring Fatty's advice about maintaining the quality of Dog's training incentives.)

Accommodation: barely holding at 1-star although She has washed my badly-repaired hammock

Entertainment: has degenerated into watching Her dance to Dog's tunes

Dog's behaviour: situation grave; Obedience School suspended AGAIN "to save money"

Her training: only cause for optimism is cat's use of Dog to train Her

Dogwatch: reinstated as critical given new arrivals

Wednesday, 3rd December: *Girlies on their knees*

Today, She turned my house (lounge, to be exact) upside down for "a photo shoot." Something to "kill two birds with one stone," as She put it. The "birds" relate to Dog of course. The "stone" to Sheldon, commandeered by Her to take "professional stills" for Her company Christmas card ("Clients will *love* it, Puss!") and Dog's "portfolio." The latter to comprise squirrelously untruthful pictures of Dog as a pooch perfect for Her to wow *PetStars,* whether or not they want to see them ("Doggy's such a rare breed, I *know* they will!" She told Fatty.)

She rushed us through breakfast, then dragged Dog off for a brush. I adjourned to my igloo for an after-breakfast nap where I slept until rude awakement by the bizarre quack quack of our new doorbell. (A few weeks ago She bought a Plug 'n Go Wireless Door Chime after Fat Fiona complained, "Three years is long enough to repair an unadulterated unexpurgated doorbell!)

My ears pricked as I heard Her thump down the hallway and open the door to the familiar breathiness of camp-as-20-pink-tents Sheldon blowing out a "Dahhling, how are you, Sweetims Pie?"

I heard a pause, then Sheldon's tee hee before he added, "Or more to the point, Dear Heart, WHAT are you?" I raised my head wondering -- what did Sheldon mean by that? Not Halloween revisited, I recall shuddering.

"Don't be *so* dense, Shell," She replied humourlessly. "You know exactly what I am; you've never seen one in a pinstripe suit before, that's all."

I purred relief. At least She wasn't doing another insulting impersonation of a cat. Except that I realised -- She was just crazy enough to dress up as a cat dressed up as Herself!

"They don't wear blinking Christmas tree earrings either, Sweetims." Sheldon chuckled.

"Sheldon, it's for a company Christmas card, remember? She was all businesslike and hot to trot, albeit a little awed. "That camera's like something from the Ark!"

"Positively modern, Dahhhling, from the 1940's when dearly departed Daddims was moonlighting as a wedding paparazzo." Sheldon's voice dripped with pride. "Now where's the doggerelle?"

"Waiting in the lounge in her Santa Claus sack," Her voice had brightened, now that Sheldon was getting down to business. "Follow me."

I couldn't visualise Dog waiting for anyone in a Santa Claus sack. This I had to see. As I jumped down from the bed, I heard Her shout, "You toerag!" She was fuming already. Sheldon was chortling. I sprinted down the hallway towards the kitchen and stopped in front of the lounge door. It was wide open and in front of me was a huge empty space. All our lounge furniture had been moved back towards the walls. In the centre was a solitary diningroom chair and Dog, plumped down beside something resembling an unrolled bin bag on the carpet. Except the bag was red with a suspicious looking wet mark on it (I could smell Dog's wee) and She was kneeling on the carpet, blotting it with paper towel.

Most extraordinarily, She was wearing a pinstriped jacket and short skirt with a pretension to reindeer antlers on her head. Dog, who looked blow dried after a bath, was sitting with Its back to Her, scratching. Guffaws of the Sheldon kind sallied forth from underneath something reminding me of a taller version of the Lying Hound's trouser press with a blanket thrown over it. Nothing but Sheldon's legs were visible.

Without any warning his head popped out from under the blanket. "Look, Sweetims, ditch the Santa sack, put fluffy chops on the chair and we'll shoot *The American Gothic* without the pitchfork, okay?" Pink-tent's face was creased, he was desperately trying not to laugh, which was when he caught sight of me in the doorway. "Hey there, Pussykins, come join the fun," he waved. "I've already got two girlies on their knees!"

Friday, 5th December: *What unsuspecting prey?*

Grrr! Prrr! Grrr! She is *not* "done with men." Else why would She change outfits three times and put on make-up (detests it) to go out for a "quick drink" at an unnamed hotel in an unnamed location with an unnamed person this evening? In the past She'd volunteer infinitely more information about Her social life than I've had any desire to know. Now She's saying nothing. *Who* or *what* is She going to see?

I absolutely will *not* countenance another Lying Hound coming into my house without screening him first. But judging from the flurry of preparations, She is definitely going out on the razzle. I haven't witnessed such a production in months. Saw it all from my igloo bed.

It took Her two false starts to get dressed. She kept asking my advice too until a fit of exasperation overtook her and she announced that "something boring but understated elegant black will have to do." She threw on a black roll-neck jumper over a pair of snug-fitting black trousers. Would have looked positively funereal had it not been for the gold chain and drooping earrings She added to an otherwise sombre ensemble. Such earrings are Her "trademark" says Fat Fiona. Zara is scathing: "Long and dangly went out with Dallas." Whatever that obscure comment means.

By the time She was trussed up to the neck, I had jumped out of the igloo to assess Her progress from the end of the bed. She was at her dressing table opposite. A large mirror hangs on the wall over it so I could see myself sitting there and Her grimace while chattering on: "Oh gawd, make-up! I hate plastering my face with powder and potions, Puss. A monumental waste of time and money. Where *is* that cosmetic case?"

She was rummaging around in a drawer for the all-in-one make-up case presented by Zara ages ago, during the supremely-well-kept woman's fruitless campaign to give Her a makeover. (This involved an "obscenely expensive" shower of beauty enhancing products which ended up in Her bottom drawer, after which Zara told Her to "forget marriage and go for cohabiting with a caveman personality with bad eyesight and dulled pheromonal sensitivities.")

"Ah ha, here it is, Puss!" Triumphant, She held up a small rectangular black case. "Right, a dash of powder, roses in the cheeks, a touch of lipstick and that is absolutely all I'm putting on for a total stranger!"

As if she instantly had second thoughts about that statement, She whipped around to face me. "Yes, I should spend hours, instead of minutes, on wardrobe and make-up for a hunting expedition. But I won't!" She went back to dabbing her face.

My ears pricked at the word "hunting." As usual She thought me interested in Her ludicrous self-justification for swimming against the tide of classical female behaviour when in fact cat's ears were upstanding at visions of the Stinking Squirrel being felled.

She suddenly slapped the top of her head, furiously trying to suppress the cowlick which had popped up. "I'll gel it down but…" She swung around to nail me again, wagged her finger and let rip: "No way am I blowing thousands on breast implants or a plastic solution for a J-Lo perfect bum!"

I sat there in Sphinx pose waiting patiently for her to blow herself out of steam, wondering what all Her fuss was about. She hurled a glance at her wristwatch. "Drat, I'm 15 minutes behind!" Then flew out of the bedroom but before I could return to my igloo, She shoved her head back through the doorway. "Sooty, I've shut doggy in the office," She big-smiled at me. "You'll have free reign of the house tonight!" With that She slammed her way out the door.

Contented smugness wells up inside me at the thought of Dog shut in Her office while I am footloose and fancy free. The worm is turning. Her training *is* moving forward after all and Dog will learn its place. But what unsuspecting prey is *She* going after?

Saturday, 6th December: *A rude awakening*

I was right, She's not done with men. Early this morning the infamous Zara trotted through our front door like a gem-stoned poodle strutting off to Crufts. She ripped Her out of bed by pummelling our door chimes. Discourteously woke me up aided by Dog's vicious albeit muffled-from-the-office barking. Next thing I knew poodle woman was prancing down the hallway past our bedroom towards the kitchen demanding an early morning cappuccino and "blow-by-blow of the hippopotamus-skinned blind date you didn't tell me about in your last email, Dahhhling!"

Her response was to stumble back into the bedroom in her elephant pyjamas (Thank goodness -- or is it a shame -- She didn't wear her threadbare, holes-under-the-armpits Zizzz nightshirt as Zara would have dropped Her like a stone) and, looking exceptionally bleary eyed and cowlicked, grab Her bathrobe off the back of the door.

"Zaraaa, it's only eight-oh-bloody clock in the morning for pity's sake." She was whining like a dog who'd lost its bone as she sloped out of the room. "Couldn't you have called first?"

By now She should know -- Zara never calls first. Prefers grand entrances, like a pretentiously pedigreed Angora who darkens the hole of unsuspecting mice. I hoped Zara would get out of Her everything I had a right to know. So I jumped out of my igloo to scamper after Her. Dog was sequestered in the office.

As I crept into the kitchen, Zara was pelting Her with questions. "So who is this character? How did you meet? Where did you go? You didn't give him your address, did you? You DID make him pay, I hope!"

Zara was pacing back and forth in front of the lounge door. I paused to sit down in the doorway and study these polar opposites of the human female: Poodle prissy Zara, fluffing up like a great white Sulphur Crested Cockatoo, versus the Scrufts Family Dog.

She said nothing; indeed Her expression was positively Chow-like: inscrutably Chinese, indecipherable.

"Cat got your tongue?" asked a smirking Zara who'd caught sight of me.

Straightening up and yawning, She finally spoke, "Zara, it's Saturday, still the middle of the night as far as I'm concerned..."

"Ah, so you *did* have a late night," Zara finger wagged. "Verrrry naughty, not the way forward on a first date. By the way Dahhhling, you really must buy yourself a proper cappuccino machine. I cannot be doing with foil packets."

"I don't want a cappuccino machine," She had started making herself a mug of tea.

"Oh, what *am* I going to do with you? Workaholic, no make-up, no cappuccino machine, elephant pyjamas and

…and a flea-bitten cat who sleeps on your bed. Do you really think any man's going to go to bed with *that*?" Zara waved bejewelled fingers in my direction causing me to meow loudly and dart forward to rub violently against one of her trousered ankles. "Ugh! Why do they always come to me? My skin crawls!"

"That's exactly why they *do* come to you, Zara, to *make* your skin crawl. And Sooty is NOT flea bitten!" She stepped towards Zara and leaned down to scoop me up into her arms. "Don't listen to her, Pussycat," She cooed, lifting me to face Her. "She's only a prissy Poodle, insanely jealous of our 15-year relationship." She planted a kiss on the tip of my nose and turned a sickly sweet smile on Zara whose mouth hung open.

My ears shot skyward, a "grrr-ow" of surprise escaped my mouth. *She* had read my mind with 100% accuracy, which poses a potential problem: such precision well honed could sabotage my master plan to bring Her to heel.

Sunday, 7th December: *Seeking "a precocious brat"*

The romantic plot thickens, not that the squirrelous Zara knows any more about Her tryst two nights ago. She sent Zara packing within minutes of the "flea-bitten" slur. This morning however I got to the bottom of Her secret-squirrel liaison when she rang Fat Fiona on hands-free in the office to tell her about the "blind date." (She is very definitely seeking a Lying Hound replacement. I only hope She's raised Her breed standard!)

She confessed to placing a personal ad in a magazine "for discerning adults" called *Happy Hunting* three weeks ago and in top-secret-squirrel style has been sifting through responses ever since! No mention to me!!!

All news to Fatty, too, who was audibly rankled. Invisible policewoman truncheoned Her with questions before scolding, "You do realise, such ads are like fishing in ponds of slippery eels?"

"I wasn't born yesterday, Fi," Her mild irritation was pushing papers around the desk. "I've worked in advertising, remember? It's full of slime balls *and* pathological liars."

"So, what'd you advertise for?" Fatty was interrogating once more.

"A precocious brat with the skin of a hippopotamus and the patience of an angel. Rather clever, don't you think?" She was all smiles and wags as she leaned back in her chair surveying a neatly stacked pile of papers.

"You want a *what*?" Incredulity from the phone.

"A man who's *not* staid and boring," She fired back.

There was a slight pause at the other end of the line before Fatty replied, "Have you met 'a precocious brat' then?" Followed by heavy breathing. I literally felt Fatty's ears prick; could imagine her tongue hanging out, too.

"Possibly," She volunteered. After which it took Fatty ages to pry out of Her a skeleton of the truth -- a 6'1" retired professional footballer turned sporting-goods salesman whose name She refused to divulge, said "It's early days!" I can't believe She won't tell *me*!

The "possibly" precocious brat introduced himself on her mobile in a "come-to-bed voice" with a message that said only "less is more" and a phone number. The voice

160

cracked Her wide open. She told Fatty it conjured up images of "Marlborough Man riding a 16-hands stallion across the Western Prairie." Why do human females swoon over tough and inarticulate?

Well, She was intrigued enough to ring him and agree to meet although "horrified at first sight of the package." Mind you, She was grinning as she said this before adding, "Looked like an American grease monkey, Fi (became lemon-faced). Had a gold medallion around his neck. Ghastly dress sense – was wearing a faded blue work shirt and tattered jeans."

"But what did *he* look like? " Fatty asked. I could hear the Marlborough Man mention had intrigued her. More panting had started after that.

"Oh, a cross between a young Marlon Brando and Matt Damon, I guess." A sharp intake of breath from Fatty. "With slicked-back dark hair and one lock falling over his forehead." She was leaning back in her chair gazing at the ceiling. A distinct smile teased her mouth.

"So the brat's a hunk, any brains?" Policewoman was back on the case but hadn't ditched the heavy breathing.

"Read English literature at university." She answered. I haven't seen Her that beaming for years!

"A dish in the rough," Fatty was surely drooling.

To which She replied with that word again, "Possibly, if you like toy boys."

There's the rub. The prospective precocious brat is, by Her calculation, more than 10 years Her junior. She's worried about accusations of "cradle snatching" and ended by telling Fatty She was "still thinking about whether or not to go out with him again."

Which is unadulterated unexpurgated codswallop. She told Fatty "the brat" also plays golf and as soon as she hung up the phone, She asked, "Where's my old golf glove, Soot?" (She's an ex-athlete herself.)

Grrr-ow! A Lying Hound replaced by "a precocious brat" does not sound like a quantum leap forward to me! Does he like or dislike cats? Above all, where's he going to sleep? Of course, I could be jumping ahead of myself. He's only met Her once and couldn't possibly have any idea what he's in for, could he? Then again, he could hate dogs. Prrr! Prrr! Prrr!

After thought: I think Her replacement-hound actions are driven by the fact She's on her own, business is bumpy, Her once-hectic social life has virtually been cancelled by Dog and She will not be with family this year at Christmas. Meaning She's feeling impoverished, insecure, unattached and unloved. Precisely why She shouldn't under any circumstances pursue another dog right now. She'll only attract flea-ridden strays.

Tuesday, 9th December: *Dog barks, She listens*

A very bad fur day. Dog refused to stay outside after She banished It to the back garden to get It off my back. Same problem as yesterday. It barked non-stop to come back in, especially when It saw me in the kitchen window. Worse, today It figured out how to put a podgy paw through my cat flap to pull open the door! She is elated at this "incontrovertible proof of the Chow's intelligence." I whip my tail in bugstration.   So much for *Pooch Perfect's* misinformation about Chows being the second stupidest breed in existence. It obviously doesn't lack reasoning power.   Grrr-ow! A brainy dog is an ill wind.

Her Pavlovian response to this barking is the latest example of Its increasing manipulation of Her. When Dog woofs, She not only listens but jumps to attention; doesn't want to upset the neighbours by allowing It to carry on. The writing is on the wall: It will bark Her into obedient compliance with all Its wishes, or scratch doors down trying.   GRRR-OW! I have enough training problems without Dog muddying the waters.

After It let itself back into the house this morning, I had to fight my way out into the garden later because She hadn't bothered putting Dog into Her office when she left to do an errand. Was too busy "thinking" about what She's already decided to do about the "precocious brat!" Left me at the mercy of Dog who was wandering aimlessly around the kitchen looking to stick Its nose into something, which something was me!

As I entered the kitchen to exit past the rubbish bin and barstool (She did get that right!), Dog padded towards me and plonked itself down in front of the barricade. Every time I tried to walk by, It batted me with a paw. I wasn't sure I could scurry past unscathed so I stopped in mid-stride and hissed. That had no impact whatsoever on Its paw-batting. I tried growling. More paw-batting. I tried deeper growling. More paw-batting. Prolonged growling with back arched, intermittent spitting and tail mega-swishing. That proved an exceptionally bad move, a red-

red-rag-to-a-bully bad move. Dog took a flying pounce at my tail! Marginally reminiscent of cat's ill-fated swipe at the Stinking Squirrel.

I was so shocked by Its cheek I turned round and scampered off. Which was far worse than my exceptionally bad move. Dog thought I wanted to PLAY and started chasing me down the hallway. Can you imagine? That furry upstart thinking A Superior Cat would stoop so low! Well, I'm convinced It did, giving me no choice but to leap up onto the bookcase near the front door. It tried jumping up after me but fell backwards onto the floor, clawing a few books off the shelf. I crouched down and in that moment with my tail swishing from side to side, I knew -- the civil war had begun.

Either I've got to get really physical and stand my ground (even if I have to gore Its beady eyes out) or give in to forever being chased at times and into places *not* of my choosing.

Note: Sheldon dropped by with proofs of the photos he took. She's "disappointed" that Dog's hind quarters don't look as "full and fluffy" as they should after Its Guy Fawkes Night shearing. Sheldon told Her not to worry: he knows "military experts" who specialise in "airbrushing classified material" – they'll add more fur to Dog's backside so no one will know it's not Dog. Wish they'd airbrush Dog *out* of the picture!

Thursday, 11th December: *No greater majesty*

A cold, wet slug of a night. I am lying exhausted in my sagging hammock, after a long day of being shadowed by the oppressive pawstomper. She and It are presumably asleep in Her room and the bedroom door is closed, thank goodness.

My hammock was virtually a no-go zone all day with Dog sniffing and pawing at me every time It passed. The badly-sewn-up corner is coming apart because She shrunk the sheepskin cover in the wash. As for Her pretence of repairing my igloo bed – which I find hard to sleep in when Dog's present, it looks shark attacked

Bugstration! Have yet to be reunited with Petronella. Another attempt failed this afternoon -- and after Dog ruined my visiting plans two days ago when It chased me up onto the bookcase. I had to stay there napping until the late afternoon when She returned from her "errand." By then it was too dark to go in search of Silver Puss. Grrr-ow! (Some "errand." She was gone for hours. Another secret-squirrel tryst?)

On top of which She sank to a new low at dinnertime. Ran out of cat food *and* tins of tuna chunks; none to be found anywhere, which is an unpleasant first. As a last resort, She offered me dog food! Initially, I refused to eat it on principle until I saw I could do so on the floor by the fridge -- in the presence of Dog's twitching black nose pressed against the other side of the glass panes of the closed door to the hall. Slowly, succulently, I licked my chops in Its furry face after every bite. Prrr! Its fresh tripe and chicken all meat loaf in jelly was surprisingly tasty.

On reflection this experience compels me to wonder -- have I unwittingly discovered a new battle tactic? Attacking Dog's food supply? Could I systematically eradicate

Its uneaten meals, empty and polish with my tongue its bigger-than-mine D-O-G engraved bowl until It starves to death? All executed under cover, when She isn't but It *is* looking? With cat's voracious appetite driving the strategy forward? Aided by a new mantra, *Heaven hath no greater majesty than a cat revenging?*

Saturday, 13th December: *Match-mating failure*

MEGA GRRR-OW! This time my hopes of searching out Petronella were dashed to mouse droppings by Cowboy Bebop. The cattle-creeping Corgi showed up for a late morning coffee with Mrs Houndslow. I got shut in Her bedroom as a "precautionary measure" to ensure Dog's compliance with *House Rule No. 4 i.e. The dog will not be permitted to gang up on me with other neighbourhood dogs.* Moments later I heard Her buzzing, "Hi there, Cowboy!" All waggy tails. "Pearl, lovely to see you, too…"

Thereafter an outburst of sniffing worked its way across the bottom of the bedroom door embroidered by the barely visible tip of a white paw trying to squeeze underneath as the sniffing increased in intensity. The imaginary stench of dusty cows welled up in my nostrils and I growled. "Bebop, stop that, come here!" It was Mrs Houndslow's bird twitter. In an instant the paw was gone.

I heard Her hustle them down the hallway and out the back door of the kitchen. Minutes later my ears pricked to faint snatches of a rising crescendo of angry "Bad dogs" from Mrs Houndslow intermingled with General Patton commands from Her. All was not roses in the garden and a short time later I heard Her stepping back down the hallway, lots of pantings and apologies behind.

"I'm so sorry about all that," Alleged owner was flooding embarrassment. "She's usually so good with other dogs."

"Oh, don't blame your Chow," smarted Mrs Houndslow who sounded stiffly piqued. "Bebop's behaviour was frightful!"

It turns out Bebop began humping Dog as soon as they were introduced and the Chow did a Rottweiler. Only minor ear scratching resulted but coffee was abandoned. Based on Dog's track record so far, I doubt sex and babies will ever be high on Its agenda. And if She and It keep me imprisoned in the house forever, it'll never get off mine!!! Not that I've got much left to work with. Grrr-ow! Grrr-ow!

Monday, 15th December: *Ungrateful little wretch*

A slippery overcast day which -- Prrr! Prrr! -- ended on a distinctly sunny note. All because Dog didn't go into leaps and bounds of joy over Her receipt of a licence to exercise It in the grounds of a private park belonging to some kind of philosophical society. I am savouring the memories of it, which started after morning walkies when Dog cavalierly took over the bedroom to lie down, totally ignoring cat's first rights of refusal to use it for morning naps.

With Dog having invaded my space, I retired to the hammock to witness arrival of the letter approving the licence application. After which I saw Her futile striving to elicit an enthusiastic response from Dog by shoving the letter in Its face and exclaiming about all the benefits of walkies there i.e. "lots of trees, a big field to run around in, other dogs to play with, no cars to worry about." All of which She relayed hunched over on all fours by Dog's nose. It didn't give Her an eye flutter.

Crestfallen but having sensed my presence in the doorway, She looked to me for crumbs of recognition and reward. "Hey there, Pussycat, isn't it great?" That's when Dog's head shot up like a squirrel belting treeward. To my astonishment She read Its mind before I did. "Oh no you don't, don't even THINK about it!" She snarled, grabbing Dog by the collar although It fought its way up to a sit.

She was no longer smiley smiley either. Rather, pissed off by Dog's lack of outward appreciation for Her efforts on Its behalf (notably, much "lobbying behind the scenes" as never more than one or two licences are approved during the year, I heard Her tell Fatty). I'm sure Dog's seeming ingratitude contributed to the boa constrictor grip She took of its collar while smiling ever more lovingly at me. "It's all right, Puss, I've got her." This remark inspired me to stroll serenely towards them meowing.

Her fierce determination to keep Dog in its place drew me closer until I leapt up onto the bed with a burst of more contented meowing. As I turned to lie down, I saw Her force marching the wriggling Chow away from the bed. The battle of wills was enjoined and I purred loudly to compliment Her breathy swearing, "Ungrateful little wretch," as She strode resolutely out of the room.

It pleases me no end to note: When the company Christmas cards arrived late this afternoon, She dumped them unopened in a corner of the office with a "harrumph."

<u>Tuesday, 16th December:</u> *What's new pussycat?*

This evening Her consultant friend Saffron came over to discuss some kind of money-making scheme called "creativity workshops." Saffron is what She calls an executive coach and part-time yoga instructor. Forever advising Her to "get into *Hatha* and juicing and stop eating anything with a face." All this to "detox oneself of negative energies." Saffron's reed thin with unruly shoulder-length black hair. Reminds me of a Shih Tzu dog with large feathery ears. Wears lots of flowing robes over sandals. A far cry from perfectly coiffed Poodle Prissy Zara who swans around in "obscenely pricey" trouser suits with a layered face and body parts dripping gold this and gold that, if not "rocks which are the real thing, Dahhhling." (In hindsight She has an amazing ability to make friends with extreme opposites who'd probably kill each other on sight.) Today, Saffron was swathed in orange and yellow, like Buddhist monks I've seen on TV.

The good news is − Saffron sees Dog from my perspective! I know this from what happened today when they were sitting at the dining table in our lounge discussing "how to put people in better touch with their animal instincts and creative impulses." (I find this enterprise hugely ironic given humans spend years beating animal instincts and gut feelings *out* of us "pets.")

She expressed doubts about rousing the creative instincts of "a bunch of deadbeats in international banking." At which point Saffron fluttered up from the table and waltzed towards me, where I was perched on top of Her upright piano to observe. I'd managed to sneak past Dog, whose head was plugging my cat flap yet again.

"Saffron, what *are* you doing?" She was leaning back in her chair, bug-eyed and bemused.

"Releasing my creativity, aren't I, Sooty," chirped Saffron dancing in front of me before breaking into rapturous song, "What's new pussycat, woah woah wo ho..." But Saffron was stopped dead in her tracks by Dog who whizzed into the lounge, such is the awesome power of the "pussycat" word. Within seconds It had sniffed me out on the piano and was grasping the keyboard with its stubby paws.

She instantly leapt to my defence growling, "Tamba, down - leave Sooty alone." Rushed over to grab Dog's collar and yank it back down onto the floor with a deep-throated "Bad dog!"

While She escorted Dog out of the room, Saffron offered me a sympathetic pat on the head and chuckled after Her, "There are no bad dogs, honey bunny, only out-of-control owners. Isn't that right, Sooty?"

I rubbed my nose against Saffron's arm as she gently stroked me along my back.

"It's not that black and white," She replied imperiously, striding back into the lounge, trying not to scowl.

"It *can* be with the right technique to interrupt bad behaviour," Saffron spoke with the confidence of one who's fought alligators and won.

"Such as?" Her raised eyebrows challenged Saffron in mid stride. Was She offended by unwelcome memories of the late Dawgsbody's tut tut letter?

"Newspaper intimidation, my dear," Saffron announced with her chin in the air. "It set my sister's pussycat free."

PRRR! My tail flapped in anticipation as Saffron described the technique in minute detail.

Wednesday, 17th December: *Newspaper intimidation*

Prrr Maximus! *They* stumble who run fast at me -- Dog has been sound blasted into submission by "newspaper intimidation." This happened today after breakfast with: It attempting more batting practice in my hammock; me growling at Its "bad behaviour"; Her rising up out of office chair with rolled-up newspaper in hand, as per Saffron's instructions, to issue warning bark, "Tamba, get down."; It paying not the slightest attention, only straining harder to gain pawhold on hammock; me furring up and batting back at It; Her moving forward irate, waving newspaper and growling menacingly, "Tamba, I said DOWN!"; Dog taking no notice; Her launching parrot shriek, "Get your damn paws off Sooty!"; Dog's blanket refusal to comply.

Prompting Her swift collapse to floor beside Dog with overhead smash of rolled-up newspaper onto ground with force of perfectly placed LIGHTNING BOLT producing ear-splitting THUNDERCLAP without touching single hair on Dog's body, dealt with such a ferocious "THAT'S ENOUGH!" that Dog dropped to floor like felled water buffalo and crawled under hammock to hide; with me observing cowering furball through new hole in bottom of falling-apart-again hammock; followed by cancellation of batting practice for rest of day and me purring sweetly to reward Her for conduct becoming an owner, never mind only "alleged." PRRR MAXIMUS MAXIMUS!!!

Friday, 19th December: *Dog is subjugated*

PRRR! PRRR! PRRR! Dog is assiduously avoiding me and the hammock. I think It views newspaper bashing on a par with fireworks, gunfire and other loud bangs combined. Thank goodness, It doesn't run behind Her desk; otherwise, the new strategy would be binned. There's only one downside to this defensive action – recurrence of Her knee pain during the floor drop to deliver the slam-bang. I remember seeing Her wince after the first "That's enough!" smash and babble. She's thoroughly convinced old field hockey injuries are the cause. Saffron disagrees, says Her painful knees are "a psycho-spiritual sign of inability to step forward and move on from the past." I agree with Saffron.

Saturday, 20th December: *Identifying "flash points"*

The day started off with a satisfying bang: Her reminding Dog of the error of any planned forays near my hammock! After breakfast It had shown signs of recovering from the initial shock of newspaper intimidation i.e. Dog began cruising ever closer to the hammock while She was working in the office. However, It failed to notice Her eagle eyes upon its every movement. As soon as It ventured my way, She rose up like a hawk citing prey. Only She had a rolled-up newspaper under her wing. "Tamba!" She growled. Dog looked up to see Her standing in the doorway wagging the newspaper in Its direction. "DON'T

172

GO THERE!" After which She cracked the paper against the office door frame. It winced and bolted past me towards the kitchen.

Saffron has advised Her to keep rolled-up newspapers or magazines within easy reach of "identified flash-points" i.e. areas where Dog is most likely to misbehave like my hammock, Her bedroom, the kitchen and terrace. She's also to watch out for "behavioural patterns that emerge at particular times of day," such as after breakfast, after Its return from walkies, etc so She can swoop down and deal a preventive slam-bang even *before* It raises a paw.

Saffron is one of Her more useful acquaintances.

Sunday, 21st December: *She needs paw bashing*

Not good news. After months the Lying Hound has resurfaced like an algae-covered serpent slithering up from the deep. The wretched man called Her early this evening when she was in the lounge reading. Dog was in the back garden so I could tuck into my dinner unmolested. I didn't hear the conversation; only saw Her walk out of the room with a tear-stained face at the end of it. After which I followed her into the bedroom where She was draped over the bed like a distressed feline. When I jumped up onto it, She reached out moaning: "Oh, Pussycat, why did he have to call?" I stiffened at the "he" word. Knew precisely who "he" was even before She elaborated. "He said he's stopped smoking, feels badly for walking out."

I thought but didn't say, "A bit late for apologies." Then She went quiet on me, lying on her side stroking my head. That's when I recalled something Fat Fiona told Her about advertising for male companionship before Christmas -- there's "a significantly higher probability of hooking a slime ball because they're *all* out to get free turkey dinners plus all the trimmings and as many presents as possible, preferably in cash form!"

What does the Lying Hound want? If he's genuinely trying to make amends (I don't believe it), then why didn't *he* send Her flowers? I ask because yesterday She received a small bouquet from the mysterious Precocious Brat whose appearance I only learned about this afternoon during Her chat with Fatty. While I was out for a wander, the Brat dropped in unannounced "between sales calls." She was taken totally by surprise, saying to Fatty she looked like "a dog's breakfast" when he showed up. Wasn't very happy about it either -- dismissed his flowers as "a wilted after-thought on the way out of a petrol station."

Sometimes I think She needs a good paw bashing by a man-size version of Dog because Her attitude strikes me as greatly lacking in graciousness or appreciation. Hoards of other men aren't exactly knocking Her door down or giving her any kind of thoughts whatsoever, after or otherwise, except for the Lying Hound whose motives are suspect in my humble opinion as A. S. Cat.

When will She ever learn -- even women are masters of their fate!!!

Tuesday, 23rd December: *Appearances are deceiving*
More insanity – Christmas Drinkies for Dogs! Yes, it really happened at lunchtime today. I was napping on the kitchen

counter when She rushed in fizzing, "Hey, Puss, we're going to doggy's first Christmas party in the little park." Gave me a pat then knelt down to open one of the kitchen cupboards. She frowned momentarily before getting up holding a bulging carry bag. "I hope she doesn't do another runner!" After which She paused for a moment's thought before leaving the kitchen.

"That would be too good to be true," I purred, tail flapping the counter where I could see right down the hallway to the front door. A few minutes later my ears pricked to the scuffles of their departure. Through half-closed lids I saw Dog being pulled outside. It was wearing a huge red ribbon tied in a bow around its neck and a Santa Claus hat which It was vigorously trying to shake off. She was wrestling with Dog whilst trying to keep hold of the carry bag. I had a modicum of sympathy for the Chow. (The first Christmas after I'd permitted Her to adopt me, She tried that ribbon rubbish on me. One well-aimed extended clawswipe across the top of Her hand, which almost drew blood, put an immediate stop to it! Of course, Dog lacks my manual dexterity.)

Without them under foot, I was able to enjoy a pleasant afternoon. All too short. They bustled back through the front door in no time, after the sky had darkened into a drizzling rain. "We're baaaaack," I heard Her singsonging as I lay in my hammock, raising my head in annoyance.

"We had a great time, didn't we, Pupsydoodle?" She turned around and I followed her with my eyes to gaze upon Dog. Only it wasn't Dog but an infinitely smaller four-legged drowned rat which smelled canine. I jettisoned up onto all fours like a bat out of hell.

"Sooty, what is it?" She was baffled by my reaction. At least I'd terrified The Thing -- it tried to run off down the hallway towards the kitchen until She yanked it backwards. "Pussycat, Pussycat," She knelt down to pat me. I'd been growling until the mists of my shock at this new intruder cleared and I saw not a rat's tail but a curled-up rat's tail riding high on The Thing's back and a slicked-back red-brown face with familiar crags down the forehead and across the snout.

It was Dog after all but Dog as I'd never seen Dog: drenched, shrunken, soaked beyond recognition! In that moment I realised -- Its normal outward appearance is exceptionally deceiving. In the dry Dog appears to be at least three times its actual size; whereas, in the wet – Triple Prrr! -- Dog is not much bigger than me! A supremely significant fact in my considerations of brute force to educate It. Plus I've discovered -- releasing a pro-active, highly aggressive, instantaneous arched-back Mega Growl has the potential to terrify Dog into a runner without, and this is important, shedding a single drop of blood, or even spit!

Thursday, 25th December: *A damp squid of a day*

Grrr-ow! Scumbugs! It's been a "dog's dinner" of a Christmas. A sodden near freezing day which I had to spend with snuffling, flu-ridden Her and the sneezing Chowpat instead of going off to my 5-star cattery.

Until this year She has always been either out of the country visiting family or away with friends for a week or more. (The Lying Hound preferred spending Christmas on a beach somewhere so he could smoke his lungs off!) She would leave me behind to enjoy the luxury of split-level accommodation at *The Cat's Whiskers,* located in farm country close to where we live. Naturally, it's 5-star and I usually take a corner room with sleeping chamber upstairs (including Danish design snuggle bed) and play area downstairs with chair and remote-controlled, life-size mouse. It darts around squeaking when activated by staff at least once a day.

The Cat's Whiskers is clean enough for even a cat to eat off its floors (scrubbed by humans until surfaces gleam). Plus I am given one of the few rooms with a view of the central atrium which features a quite delightful garden of indoor plants and shrubs in which reside two rabbits, Piggle and Wiggly, a tortoise-shell tom Mandible and slate-grey Palm Cockatoo Basher. They are the entertainment provided for resident cats by the cattery owner, Mrs Pettypat, who's scrupulously discerning about whom she lets in – those with proper medical certificates.

On a fair day I can lie in the sun which streams down through the skylight over my bedroom or wile away hours watching the antics of Mrs Pettypat's animals. The cockatoo likes to chase Mandible and give him a good head bashing with his beak if the cat has been pawswiping at him. Piggle and Wiggly are forever trying to burrow their way out of the shrub garden to visit the guests. Since Dog's arrival I have been deprived of even one night there!

In retrospect, Christmas was bound to be iffy. She has been "financially challenged" (Her euphemism for "living off capital instead of revenue") all year as well as "socially incapacitated" by her new status as a "single working pet mum" (between boyfriends), as She once described herself to Zara. I must admit -- Her whole life *has* revolved around Dog. She hasn't given a single dinner party since Its arrival. Or even had people in for drinks unless Mint Tea with Saffron and coffee with Fatty count.

Last night we were supposed to have had neighbours over for mulled wine and She had planned to go off to Fat Fiona's today for Christmas lunch. But all the plans went pear-shaped when She woke up yesterday morning with a raging headache, fever and chills. "I can't face Christmas this year, Puss," She groaned at me before cancelling all her arrangements.

If truth be known, I think She's been wanting an excuse to avoid it. The Lying Hound stomped out of her life right after Christmas last year. His phone call a few days ago must have brought back upsetting memories. Explains Her recent moodiness. Of course, leaving all Her Christmas shopping to the last minute didn't help. I had to listen to unending complaints about "the crowded shops and outlandish cost of only one day out of 365 which would total over £182,000 per family on an annualised basis!" Dog's been under the weather too. Sneezing and off its food lately. Women! No staying power in wet or cold weather conditions.

Neither am I impressed by Her present buying this year. Not that I'm precious about anything so pedestrian as Christmas gifts and counting up who got what (Christmas being an excuse for gross human excess at a certain time of year). But the facts of present distribution speak for themselves:

Presents for Cat = 3
1. Small tin of Good Boy **catnip** drops *(Yuk!)*
2. Carpet cat **scratching post** *(After 15 years?)*
3. **Flying fish** attachment for scratching post
   (Why not flying Dog ?)

Presents for Dog = 7
1. Water-proofed-back **towel**
1. Rolled-leather dog **collar**
2. Ergonomically-designed Maxi **slicker brush**
3. Tin of blueberry pawscotti **biscuits** from
   Sniffers Bakery
4. Unidentified **special treats**
5. Animal **healing CD** to reduce distress at
   distressing sounds
6. **Overstuffed donut dog bed!!!!!**

Fine, She bought us presents. But WHY another overstuffed dog bed??? Doesn't She ever listen? Dog's breeder was unequivocal -- Chows sleep when and where they please. This does not include institutionalisation in beds -- puffball, donut or other! How can She justify squandering the savings realised from buying *me* lesser-quality cat food on purchase of yet another ruddy bed for cruddy Dog??? It's pure pigheadedness on Her part --

179

inability to accept the nature of the beast. Small wonder this Christmas was a damp squid.

Note: Early this evening the Precocious Brat phoned to wish Her a Merry Christmas (She mentioned his call to Fat Fiona who rang later to see if she was all right). I gather he offered to visit Her tomorrow if she wants any company and that She told him she "looked and felt hideous" and that he should leave her alone until after the New Year. I've no idea how he responded but if I'd been on the receiving end of such scroogy comments, I'd have given Her an ear lashing. Flu is no excuse for rudeness!

Wednesday, 31st December: *Cat's resolutions*

A dog's dessert of a New Year's Eve! I should have been able to enjoy it roaming around the house all evening munching at will on morsels of Good Doggy Fish Cake which she baked specially for "the pets" who suffered slim pickings at Christmas due to Her flu bug. But best-laid plans of mice and women often go awry.

She and Dog went to Zara's for "a small and very intimate" supper party after Zara insisted She make greater efforts to "shop for and not buy" new male companionship. (The Precocious Brat doesn't exist in Zara's mind because She's been so tight-lipped about him.) She tried crying off with the excuse that she couldn't leave Dog because of the fireworks. But Zara told her to bring Dog along so off they went early this evening leaving me with the prospect of a blissfully free run of the house.

Wishful thinking. She and Dog returned far too soon, tails between their legs.

"I knew we should've stayed home, Soot," She all but cried as she came through the front door and saw me sitting in the hallway. "What a nightmare!" She looked pale and drawn and Dog was straining towards the office. "Oh no, you don't, you are abso-bloody-lutely *not* going behind the desk!" She jerked Dog backwards and I could see Her fighting between anger and tears. I jumped back into my wonderful new fleece-lined radiator bed which young Rupert gave me for Christmas.

[I can't believe it took Her godson to replace my disgraceful hammock. The new one came with a note saying "The lady in the pet shop promised it would bring extra comfort and warmth to an ageing cat." Rupert's gift to Dog was equally thoughtful – another full-bodied little green man washing-up brush since Dog's chewed everything but the head of the old one.]

As She took off her coat, she proceeded to tell me about the unfinished New Year's Eve dinner. Midway through Zara's Beef Wellington, someone pulled a party popper which set off everyone else doing them. Dog went berzerk behind Zara's new "multi-thousand-pound" flat-screen TV and DVD entertainment centre where It began pawing the wall. At sight of Dog doing a Rottweiler on her silk wallpaper, Zara started screaming which only made Dog paw more furiously. Which made Zara order Her to remove "the filthy beast" from the premises immediately. Requiring Her to wrestle Dog out from behind the telly while Zara, too upset to watch the extraction, left the dinner table in a rage.

She was literally shaking as she recounted all the gory details to me. Dog was a cowering, salivating mess on the floor. I hadn't given much thought to the fireworks going off in our neighbourhood until I saw It going into paroxysms of ferocious panting at every distant bang. The two were in a terrible state.

It took awhile for both to calm down, during which She took off her party clothes and donned Her Zizzz nightshirt and elephant trunk slippers and announced we should "all go into the lounge to toast the New Year despite the disastrous end of the old one." I decided not to object and scampered into the room ahead of Her to make myself comfortable on the sofa. A few minutes later She struggled in with Dog and closed the door behind. She let Dog off the lead, turned on the gas fire and put Her new Mozart tape from Fatty on the stereo. Poured herself an orange-scented drink from a bottle in the cupboard beside the fireplace. I could tell She was dog tired by the way she crumpled onto the sofa beside me.

"What a year," She sighed heavily. Dog sat down by the door and slid onto its tummy before rolling over onto one side, its back towards us. She took a sip of her drink and started massaging me behind the ears. I purred to make her feel better. "What's it all about, eh Pussycat?" She asked in a deflated voice while staring into the fire. I sat up as She stroked my head and purred some more. In that moment I decided to crawl into Her lap for I realised yet again, She can't help being only human; therefore it is up to me to guide Her across the precipice of existence.

She put her drink down and leaned back into the sofa. Closing her eyes, she stroked my back until she fell asleep, her hand slowly sliding off me down to her side. I heard Dog snoring softly. It occurred to me -- both females were at long last bowed in submission to the higher power remaining vigilant amongst them.

As I stared into the fire, alone with my own thoughts, and reflected upon the nature of their inherent weak-nesses, I made these resolutions:

New Year's Resolutions
- I shall be more tolerant of Her shortcomings and peccadilloes given She is trapped in her humanity.

- I shall exploit the pre-emptive strike (bat-out-of-hell) approach to bloodless subjugation of Dog.

- Above all, as A Superior Cat, I shall act in a manner that demonstrates even greater understanding of what I see as a profound truth; namely, *frailty thy name is woman, whether human or canine.*

Follow-up notes about Christmas:

Her present from us: She claims Dog and I gave Her a lemon-scented toilet water spray which is "sneeze-proof."

Her present from the Precocious Brat: The day after Christmas he dropped a so-called Panty Rose through our letterbox. I will not tonight call Her an ungracious bitch for labelling the long-stemmed red rose wrapped in a pair of rather scant white lace knickers as "terribly CHAV" in a tone of voice similar to Zara's about Her defunct cinnamon-and-clove perfume.

Her present from the Lying Hound: Nil as far as I can see. Neither has any word been forthcoming from him since the phone call. I hope it stays that way.

January: Rats and Backward Steps

Saturday, 3rd January: *Home improvements*

A so so kind of day. After a frosty start it was sunny and bright enough for me to trot off to see if Petronella was anywhere in sight. Prrr! She was -- sitting in a first-floor window of her house. Grrr-ow! The pesky Westies were sniffing for Scotland in the garden. I had to be content with perching on the wall beneath the window to tail twitch at Silver Puss while she rubbed her shoulders back and forth against the glass panes to say hello. Can't wait to rub noses again! Predictably Mangle and Wurzel picked up my scent and started a furore of barking so I took off for home.

On returning, I found Her on the office phone with Zara. Poodle Priss rang Her on New Year's Day to apologise for being "a trifle melodramatic" about Dog's wall pawing. Turns out Husband No 4 Roger is animal friendly and ticked Zara off for her "insensitive treatment of a pet in distress." Zara apologised by sending Her a bouquet of yellow roses yesterday, along with a bowing-and-scraping sorry note and luncheon invitation to make up for her "rudeness." She is now in a more relaxed frame of mind and has told us she's made some belated New Year's Resolutions:

One: She will do "a better job of pet parenting." This will cover: taking Dog back to Obedience School; not having us "pets" make sacrifices to ease Her financial worries; and doing more to "honour Pussycat's needs" (as Saffron advised).

Two: She will spend more time with her godson (probably because Rupert said *he* wanted to spend more time with Dog!).

Three: She will avoid Lying Hounds. (About time!)

As far as "honouring my needs" goes, I expect to see reinstatement of premier-quality cat food, more ham-and-cheese special treats and receipt of the odd bit of fish cake in addition to better care of my new radiator bed. These resolutions may explain why, upon re-entering the kitchen this morning, I was able to walk freely past Dog who was sitting in the lounge behind a closed door to the kitchen. I hope it's the start of Her taking greater pains to ensure my safe passage throughout the house so I can use my new radiator bed without having to suffer Dog's panting or salivating overhead. (Possibly, She is racked with guilt following Rupert's exposure of her flagrant negligence in this area of my personal care.) The year ahead may not be as grim as anticipated.

Weather: the wet damp of December is giving way to drier cold with occasional sun. More chances to see Petronella?

Hunting prospects: chasing after the Stinking Squirrel is suspended until the spring

Food: better fare as a result of pet parenting resolution?

Accommodation: improved with new fleece-lined radiator bed gifted by Rupert (Got Her off the hook!)

Entertainment: promising if Chow continues to do Rottweilers on other prospective "playmates"

Dog's behaviour: signs of Its being brought to heel by newspaper intimidation and cat's pre-emptive strikes

Her training: positive outlook as long as She takes *consistent* approach to Dog's behaviour modification

Dogwatch: continuous monitoring essential

Monday, 5th January: *Godfatherly intervention*

Rupert called Her late this afternoon to make arrangements to visit Dog in the spring. She was in the office when he rang and put him on hands-free so She could continue working. From my new radiator bed, I could hear the entire conversation. She's trying to spend more time talking to her godson as part of Her New Year's Resolutions. But She hadn't reckoned on Rupert's interest in celebrating Dog's first birthday at the end of March.

"Can we give doggy a party?" Rupert begged Her. His voice was tinged with excitement and She was caught off guard. Could tell by the way She sat up to attention and broke out in worry lines across her face.

"Hmmm, let's see." She leaned over and flipped through the pages of her desk diary, then looked over at me. "Yes, I suppose we could. But you better check with Mummy first, Rupy. You know how nervous she gets around cats and dogs."

"Don't worry, Mummy can stay in the car if she's so scared."

She couldn't help chuckling. "Check with her first, Darling. Mummy may not want to stay in the car after driving over three hours to get here!"

"Why not? You leave doggy in the car!" Would that human adults were so logical.

"Well, talk to Mummy anyway." She said, grinning at me.

"Okay, and tell doggy I hope she starts chewing on my dish brush very soon."

Rupert has handled Dog's reluctance to embrace his Christmas present with maturity beyond his years. When She threatened to toss what's left of Dog's old dish brush, Rupert exercised his godfatherly right of intervention on the Chow's behalf, telling Her that Dog is "only trying *not* to be wasteful and finish one thing before starting another." She has left Dog to it.

As soon as Rupert hung up, Her true feelings about Dog's birthday party tumbled out. "How am I going to give a party for doggy when Rupy's got a petaphobe for a mother? It won't exactly honour *your* needs, Puss!" She got up off her chair and came over to give me a pat. I gave her a loud purr of agreement. At least She was seeing things from my perspective for a change. "Oh well, Soot, let's see what Marigold says. It may end up a non-starter."

She walked back into the office and turned around to face me before delivering some very good news. "Pussycat, you'll be pleased to know -- I'm going to have a proper outdoor kennel made for doggy. It'll cost a bomb but I'll be able to put Tamba outside all year long, whatever the weather, which should make you one happy bunny!"

Except for the bunny analogy, I am delighted by this further proof that the canine worm in our household continues turning in my direction.

Thursday, 8th January: *A pooch palace is ordered*

It's official. A bespoke outdoor kennel to serve as "an ideal retreat for a precious pooch in any season" has been ordered for Dog. She chattered on all morning about its "redwood tongue-and-groove shiplap wall cladding" while Dog gave Her not the slightest nose twitch. Either It had its chin down on its paws and hind legs spread flat out on the kitchen floor ("A sign of superior breeding," She's forever telling anyone who gives Dog's pose a quizzical look), or It was looking up at me sitting on the counter as if to ask, "What is She on about?"

Being more engrossed in licking my paws after breakfast, I only caught the odd comment about its igloo-style construction versus sloping roofs, adjustable vents, extended lounging space and other turgid specifications until She mentioned the kennel's location. Dog's "luxury pad" is to be installed on MY terrace. Grrr! I recognise She's trying to get Dog out of my way but... Grrr-ow! Precisely how big is this kennel going to be? And where exactly does She intend putting it on my terrace? I will not take kindly to losing prime sunning space to an ugly pooch palace destined to become a breeding ground for fleas, a hideout for itinerant hedgehogs or temporary den for lost fox cubs.

On top of which I can't help but wonder if Her order for "a redwood kennel with decorative coving and over-hanging roof plus shrub tubs and ornamental tree" might not go the way of the puffball and donut beds – forever unused. Christmas has come and gone and to my knowledge Dog has gone nowhere near the donut in Her bedroom although unlike the puffball bed, She has chosen not to command or encourage Dog overtly to do so.

Friday, 9th January: *A rat in the house!*

HUGE CRISIS OF GORILLA PROPORTION! She found a rat in the spice cupboard tonight -- right before bedtime when she went to make herself a cup of Mint Tea. I was nodding off in my igloo when I heard a shriek and door slam. I raised my head, Dog hurtled out of the bedroom barking furiously. Within seconds She'd rushed back into the room screaming, "A rat, Soot, in the cupboard, what'll I do?"

She was rubbing her hands together nervously, staring at me like a budgie whose cage is being pummelled by a starving cat. Then She froze and speared me with the iciest stare I've seen in years. "SOOOTY, what the hell are we doing with a rat in the house?" She was shouting at me. "It's YOUR job to keep 'em out, I don't care how old you are!" Actually pointed her finger at me.

I was beyond grrr-ows at the outburst. As if I was responsible for a problem inevitably created by humans not doing *their* jobs, like using proper bins to dispose of all their filth, not throwing food onto the ground, keeping their houses clean and gardens tidy etc. I don't know what She expected me to do about Her rat. I gave up large rodents ages ago (except for the Stinking Squirrel -- that's personal). Rats are dirty and disease ridden -- I don't care what humans say about the "sweet little white ones" they keep as pets.

Grrr-ow! She didn't wait for a reply, ran out mumbling something about getting a bucket to drop it into when She reopens the cupboard door. I knew the rat would be long gone by the time she got there. Sure enough, She shrieked again, "Oh gawd, it's gone, it's gone, where the hell's it gone to?"

Saturday, 10th January: *"Useless cat" invective*

Too rainy and cold to visit Petronella. Which sentenced me to a day of Her in hysterics over the rat sighting. She bent my ear about it from morning to night. Figures the rat ate its way through the extractor fan ducting running through part of the spice cupboard which sits over the hob area. *Question*: how did it get into the ducting in the first place? *Problem:* It did not get in via the vent on the outside wall as that's too narrow for even a small garden snake. *Horrible conclusion for Her*: the rat ate its way into the ducting from some other point *inside* the house. Hence it was able to scurry back down the ducting to make a quick escape -- to where is what She hates to wonder!

She worked herself up into such a frenzy about the prospect of a "major rat infestation" that she was positively obnoxious to me after breakfast. She was rummaging around the cupboards trying to stuff cardboard around the damaged ducting to prevent any more visitations. Thinks I didn't hear the "useless cat" invective She muttered as I watched Her from the counter. She actually turned around and almost spat at me, "It's not as if you're overworked!"

After that She was onto the Council's emergency helpline to send a Pest Control Officer out immediately. He's supposed to come on Monday. She's not happy about the delay but ours is not the only house under attack. A council employee told Her "off the record" that residential streets nearest the motorway (which include ours) are all "crawling with vermin" since they've stopped cutting the grass verges as a budget-saving measure. The verges have become overrun and whole colonies are shipping out to find new housing elsewhere.

Meanwhile She's begun bad-mouthing all the cats in our neighbourhood, including me, for having become "fat and flabby" instead of staying "lean and mean" enough to keep the rat population under control.

Of lesser importance, this afternoon Dog was taken off to the vet's to "lose its inside bits," as She put it to Saffron, whom She rang this evening to enrol in a yoga class to help reduce Her stress levels, no doubt elevated by the rat encounter. I assume losing Its bits means Dog will be permanently deprived of the chance to mate and mother successfully. Not that Dog is remotely the mating or maternal type. Strikes me as more of a female preying mantis – has sex, decapitates the male.

Sunday, 11th January: *Like a drama queen*
More theatrics! After a dog-free evening last night, we were awakened much too early by a "very snippy call" from

192

the vet demanding She pick Dog up immediately. The Chow was purportedly "acting like a drama queen" and creating havoc in frantic attempts to break out of its kennel. I could hear a strident female voice complaining that Dog had bit through its "indestructible" extendable lead and was currently barking so intensely (Even I could hear It in the background!) that the whole surgery was in "an uproar." She saw red at the "drama queen" accusation. "How dare they call my little girl that after a total hysterectomy less than 24 hours ago!" She railed on her way out the door.

A short time later She was back. I'd retreated to my hammock to get a good view of their entrance. I have to say -- Dog looked exceedingly miserable, plodding ever so slowly into the house with Its fluffy head hanging to the ground and tail uncurling behind. The normally pointy ears lay flat against its leonine head -- its reddish fur had that slightly whitish cast it seems to get when Dog's distressed.

"Poor old doggy," She said trying to soothe It down the hallway towards Her office. Dog pulled Her towards the bedroom and not having the heart to resist, She unleashed it with a sigh. I leapt out of the hammock to observe Its laboured progress. The Chow padded over to the side of the bed along the window where with very heavy movements, It eased its chunky body down onto the carpet. I hopped up onto the unmade bed to peer down at Its inert form. Sensing my proximity, Dog slowly raised its head and gave me the only truly mournful glance I've ever seen radiate from its craggy face. The normally beady black eyes were opaque and tear-stained at their corners and in that moment for the first time since Dog had come to live with us, I pitied it. The animal had not asked for "its bits" to be removed as neither had I asked for my manhood to be taken. How well I remember *that* day in the refuge. No one asked my permission, either. Simply cut off my future generations with a snip and a chuckle about "feline eunuchs." On the other hand it's been said, "Sex is a bonus." But Dog is too young to know that.

I turned around and saw Her standing in the doorway, regarding me with curiosity before a smile washed over her face. "That's right, Pussycat, you take care of doggy," She chirped. "She'll be right as rain in a day or so, with dozens of boyfriends and nothing but safe sex ahead!"

My tail flapped on the bed. I have to give Her credit -- She has an astonishing ability to look on the bright side.

Monday, 12th January: *Unwashed and furry faced*

The rat catcher showed up this morning. She'd been waiting for him in one of Her smart pinstipe business suits which She put on after vacuuming the hallway and kitchen. Told me She didn't want the Pest Control Officer thinking we're "white trash contributing to the problem." Offered him tea and biscuits as soon as he arrived.

"Don't worry, Miss," he said between munches and sips, "I'll make sure all your rats are removed." He was trying to sound gallant after Her face fell when he said he couldn't "set baits" in our kitchen and would have to "attack the colony by accessing roof spaces first." The rat catcher has told us that the "disgusting bin areas" in front of several other houses nearby already confirm the existence of "a full infestation."

Although horrified, She has promised to "crack the whip" with all the neighbours and issue written progress reports weekly until everyone has done their bit to "clean up their rubbish and whatever else" he says needs doing. I could tell by the gleam in the rat catcher's eye, he was overawed by Her take-charge attitude. Before he left, he gave her his email address, work telephone and mobile number saying She should feel free to contact him "any time of day or night" if She becomes "too unnerved by the scratching of tiny feet scurrying around in the walls."

She blanched at this comment, let out an "Oh, gawd, no!" compelling the rat catcher to touch her arm to reassure Her he was only pulling Her leg and "not to worry love" as she's probably scared our rat into going elsewhere for "its amusement." I note he avoided telling Her what we cats already know; namely, there are growing numbers of "super rats" on the block and they are more domesticated than ever!

When Fat Fiona rang this evening, She boasted somewhat wryly that if nothing else, She'd "pulled a Pest Control Officer." From my perch on the big filing cabinet I could see Her expressions as she talked to Fatty who must have asked what the rat catcher looked like. She grimaced, said he had "the unwashed and furry-faced look of someone who hasn't shaved for days."

I could hear Fatty laughing at the end of the phone. Her comments did not amuse me. What did She expect? – A clean-shaven, waist-coated stockbroker type when the poor man has to spend hours crawling around dank cellars and dusty attics to eyeball rat droppings! At least a rat catcher is a step up from a Lying Hound.

Monday, 19th January: *No prize mouser Herself*

Her first progress report about "the potentially serious health and safety issue of rats in the belfry" has gone down well with all the neighbours except the Nittypickles, an elderly couple who have two Siamese cats, Bubble and Squeak. She tried to end the report on a light-hearted note but it backfired. The Nittypickles have taken umbrage over Her facetious remark that "our cats have clearly fallen down on the job raising the question of whether or not 21st century pussies, especially toffee-nosed ones, are up to the mark." Which I do not find clever either.

The Nittypickles are demanding a written apology with copies to be sent to everyone who received the report. She doesn't know how to respond -- particularly as Mr Nittypickle, whom She saw "decluttering" his house walls of ivy this afternoon, told Her "in strictest confidence" that his Missus was "over-reacting" and secretly he agreed with Her every word. Recently, he said, he put Bubble into a coat closet after hearing scratching noises. All the Siamese did was back out of it and hide under a bookcase. He confessed that had he known the "overpriced pussies" were so lame, he'd never have agreed to buy them.

As for me, I wish She'd get off our case. She's no prize mouser Herself.

Tuesday, 20th January: *No fool I*

GRRR-OW! Today I have detected a new and more insidious-than-ever pattern to Dog's behaviour since "the operation." It surfaced late this afternoon when She went off on an errand. While napping in Rupert's hammock, I was most irritatingly awoken by a nose snuffle. I opened my eyes and there in my face was Its whisker-twitching, runny black nose and two shiny slanty eyes peering over the edge of the hammock. I jerked my head upward and gave It a hiss. Mistake. It winced then lifted a big podgy paw onto the edge.

I rose up into a fur-on-end back arch preparing to mega growl when the front door opened to Her jovial, "Hello everybody, I'm ho-ohhhme…" which stopped me. It withdrew the paw and trotted off into Her office where it lay down and rolled over onto one side facing me with flickering eyelids. By the time She'd reached my hammock, Its eyes were tightly shut and to a casual observer, It was no more guilty than a sleeping dog lying. "Hi, Puss, everything okay?" She asked leaning down to give me a chin rub.

Before I could answer, She turns around and the next thing I hear is a melted buttering of, "Ah, bless, doggy's fast asleep." After which She walks into the office where she kneels down by its side and begins patting Dog repeatedly on the head. "Are you still a poorly little girl?" She syrup drips over It. At which juncture She catches my eye and asks, "Has Tamba been like this the whole time, Soot?"

I could feel my whiskers bristle as I sat up in the hammock with my tail windshield wiping. Sensing my altered state, She then asks, "What's up with you, Puss?"

Grrr-ow! I thought but didn't say as I saw one of Dog's eyes flutter. It was frustrating watching Her fail to notice Dog's actions and I let out a deep-throated purr to tell It in no uncertain terms, It didn't fool me – not for a minute!

Friday, 23rd January: *Falsehood behind closed doors*

Dog's emerging cunning is cause for grave concern. Newspaper intimidation is rarely activated because Dog does not put a paw wrong when She's present.

This evening She went off to her first yoga class at Saffron's, leaving us home alone. Because Dog's allegedly "still fragile," She did not shut It in the office. Thus Dog was lying in the hallway at a respectful distance from me when She left. But as soon as Her car pulled out of the drive, Dog was up off the floor and nosing around my hammock. I'd been snuggled down in it and when I heard panting overhead, tried to ignore Dog by burrowing deeper into the hammock's thick fleece lining.

All It did was shove a cold wet nose into my side which, regrettably, It's big enough to do these days. I raised a warning paw and hissed. It was water off a duck's back. Within seconds It launched a double paw swipe at me! In response to which I shot up like an angry meercat blowing out a mega growl. It backed off, then crouched down on both forelegs and wriggled its head and body like a bullock pawing the ground before a charge. First It barked, then hurled itself towards the hammock.

I chose not to take the full impact of another assault by high jumping over It to shoot off towards the kitchen and what I hoped would be an unlocked cat flap. I hit the flap like a bullet. Luckily, it gave way and I shot out into the safety of the garden. Dog tried to follow but couldn't. I scampered underneath the conifer alongside the terrace. From there I could see Its nose hanging out twitching furiously to pick up my scent.

Fortunately, It didn't try bulldozing its way through the hole. But what It *did* do was almost worse -- the recalcitrant rabblebowser plugged my flap tight with its furry snout for the rest of the evening until She returned. It effectively barred my re-entry to the house on an icy cold winter's night and no one but me, the victim, had witnessed this deplorable crime against cat most foul.

It is not fear which raises my hackles but inexpressible fury at the hideous injustice of having been outted from my house after taking pity on It only a few days ago. As I lie on the edge of sleep back in my igloo bed, I ask myself – how can I expose such falsehood thriving behind closed doors?

Sunday, 25th January: *Dog's power surges*

I curse our first snowfall and freezing my paws off every time I go out for a wee; Dog revels in it. This morning I saw It rush about the fluffy white blanket tossed over our grass last night, like some hyperactive squirrel rolling around and doing somersaults. I was sitting on the kitchen windowsill fuming at the prospect of a late breakfast. Delayed so She could have a go at some yoga practice i.e.

sitting cross legged on a mat on the kitchen floor and making strange humming sounds like swarming bees as she tried wrapping herself into a pretzel and failed miserably. "It's for greater relaxation and improved health, Puss," She'd said before making a total hash of getting up into a kneeling position. Kept yelping, "Ouch!" and "Damn field hockey!" and falling back onto her bum. Until She finally got up off the floor grunting, "So much for yoga, Puss," sounding exactly how I was feeling about being unfed and unable to visit Petronella.

Afterwards She let Dog out for a pee and we both watched its antics from the window. Within minutes the Chow's face was sprinkled white, making it look like a rowdy polar bear. She went all goo goo eyed over Its "little clown" excesses. "I must get a photo of doggy enjoying her first snowfall," She twittered, disappearing to get her camera and leaving me hungrier than ever. Before long she was outside making tiny snowballs and throwing them at Dog, who opened its mouth and snapped its jaws every time one sailed by. Mistook the white powder for Parmesan cheese, in my opinion.

The disturbing aspect of all this is – falling temperatures clearly boost Its energy to uncontrollable levels. The Chow turns into even more of a tumbler who throws its weight around. No guesses as to who'll become the future target of these power surges!

Monday, 26th January: *Dog's party is a goer*

Grrr! Rupert rang this afternoon to say Marigold would drive him up in the spring to attend Dog's birthday party although she'll visit friends when Rupert stays with us. Meaning, unfortunately, the party's "a goer." She's "relieved" to be free of Marigold but already getting herself wound up about it. Started pacing the kitchen floor at teatime. "What do you think Rupy will expect me to do for Dog? " She asked me, which question preceded a dump of all Her worries: "Children's parties are serious undertakings these days. You don't just serve ice cream and cake anymore. Kids want goody bags with mobile phone cards and DVDs in them, magicians, chart music, cakes with singing candles and goodness knows what else!" All of that spewed forth while She was waiting for the tea kettle to boil. It did and She sighed, "Gawd, Puss, wish I had my events manager back!" After which She buckled down onto one of the stools and stared out the window for ages.

I remain non-plussed by the absurdity of Her anxieties. How can even She obsess over a dog's birthday party?

Tuesday, 27th January: Consciously playing games

Here we go again -- back to Obedience School! She's into the pet parenting resolution with a vengeance. Got down to it this morning when she woke up early to cook up a batch of Good Doggy Fish Cake for Dog's class this evening. Obviously, has decided to take Fat Fiona's advice about using quality incentives to motivate the "criminally intelligent."

I had refused to get up with Her at such an unsociable hour (albeit I slept in the hammock last night) but when I smelled a garlicky fishy something in the air, I thought I'd better go out into the kitchen to see what She was up to. Dog was already there angling to get its snout in the trough. "You guys are so predictable," She said when she saw me enter. She was in a reasonable mood, grinned from one to the other of us as she put various bits and pieces back into the cupboards. "One hint of tuna or sardines and you're all wiggling noses and twitching whiskers."

I jumped up onto the counter and was half crouching and craning my neck towards Her, *not* to invite advances but to get a better whiff of the sardines lying on a plate. As if reading my thoughts, She added, "Yes, Soot, you'll get a bit of fish cake, too." At least I do not have to obey a series of inane human commands first. A minor detail in the face of Dog presenting reformed behaviour when the reality is rather different.

Now more than ever I am convinced Dog is playing games with Her. Dog is a Chow and Chows are by nature *not* obedient. Yet, It was the perfect pooch at Obedience School tonight. The first dog to not only crawl all the way under a chair in only one go but scuttle under the length of two arranged side by side, She boasted to me afterwards. Dog *portrayed* itself (my word for its behaviour) as "so clever" that the *Pooch Perfect* instructor publicly acknowledged It was "a star performer who's exemplary of what's achievable with practice and persistence."

No one, certainly not Her, has mentioned the fact Dog has been enrolled in the same Level 1 course on three previous occasions. Obviously, *Pooch Perfect* would like nothing more than to string out Dog's enrolment in Level 1 for as long as possible. She will collude in this subterfuge to build Dog's reputation as a perfect pooch. Dog will use studied obedience to pull the wool over Her eyes and cover up Its squirrelous behaviour when She's absent. Thus will Dog undermine my position in the household.

Dog is no dimwit, only a corrupt manipulator of the truth that friendly eyes never see faults.

Friday, 30th January: *History in the making*

Event of the decade! Dog's new redwood kennel has arrived. A small but fancier version of a garden shed without any door or windows. Over large in my opinion and not what I envisaged as a cosy den for a wolf offshoot. At least She's had enough sense to have part of the hedge along the terrace cut out so the kennel sits back against the boundary wall and doesn't take up much of my lounging area.

There are two tubs of shrubs plus a small tree in a large pot around its entrance. After the chaps who installed it left, She spent a few minutes rearranging the tubs while I was soaking up winter sun from atop the wrought-iron table She leaves out all year long on the terrace. Dog was shut in Her office. "Right, Puss, now for the interior decoration," She said before darting back into the house, to re-emerge minutes later with two large rolls of something smelling rubbery.

"Eh voila, Soot, wall-to-wall carpeting with waterproof backing!" She informed me with a ring of good cheer in her voice. She walked briskly towards the kennel where she got down cautiously onto her knees to stuff the two rolls of carpeting through its arched doorway. Had to wriggle Her bum around to get the unrolled carpets to lie flat and seamlessly on the slatted wood floor.

Eventually, She got up to survey her handiwork, asked for my opinion, "What do you think? Is this 5-star or what?" She'd started walking back and forth in front of the kennel, stopping every few paces to gaze at the new sloped-roof structure. "I do hope pupsydoodle likes her new home!" She cast me a hopeful glance before cantering off in the direction of the house. While She was gone, I made a bet that Dog would view the new luxury kennel as no more than a hardcore puffball bed.

A few minutes later Dog bounced out the back door with Her trotting behind. "Tamba, come see your new penthouse!" She cried out. The scorned cowlick had sprouted in her excitement. As expected, Dog didn't give Her or the kennel a sideways glance. It sped across the terrace and took a flying leap off the edge, heading for the bottom of the garden. "Tamba, come HERE!" She yelled, more than mildly irritated. It flew down the stone steps of the embankment in a race to the taller of the conifers.

From my table perch I saw Dog reach the tree and rear up onto its hind legs to try pawing its way up the trunk. It was barking and I followed its gaze to see several feathery branches wave in quick succession as a familiar tree rat flew upwards from one to another. Dog was having another go at my squirrel. She was standing stoop shouldered in front of me watching Its progress. I had no pity for Her parental disappointment as I shot past to join the chase. The over-priced pooch palace is history.

<u>Saturday, 31st January:</u>   The truth about dog houses

She is gutted by Dog's rejection of the pooch palace, which cost several hundred pounds with shrubs and soft furnishings. Yesterday, after the Stinking Squirrel did a skydive out of our conifer into a tree next door, She tried bribing Dog to go inside it with a trail of Good Doggy Fish Cake leading up to the doorway. Even after It ate its way up to the entrance, Dog refused to go any further until She crawled in first and bribed It with pieces of Cumberland sausage. It climbed in halfway, took the sausage and instantly backed out still chewing.

Now Her knees "ache like hell" and She has spent most of today "doing market research" amongst dog-walker friends and owner acquaintances to find out if their dogs use kennels. The results are "dismal," She told her mother this evening after speaking to nearly a dozen people on hands-free. I was privy to all the "interviews" from my impregnable position on top of the filing cabinet.

Every dog owner She spoke to said they *did* have a dog kennel but none of their dogs ever used it! When She called up Drusilla Fence, the ex bag lady broke into peals of laughter claiming that "everyone knows dogs don't use kennels" and that "they're only a scam!"

She challenged Drusilla that some dogs must use their kennels "else people wouldn't spend money on them!"

Drusilla tried to explain that many owners are duped into buying kennels because they don't want to be seen "refusing their precious pooch one because the dog *might* not use it" nor do they want to admit later to having spent loads of money on "one which Rover never uses!"

She remained unconvinced. "But people *did* admit this to me, today, when I rang them," she argued.

Drusilla was unperturbed. "Of course they did, they know you're one of them now!"

I could tell She was sizzling at Drusilla's know-it-all tone and couldn't resist trying to get clever, which tactic was destined to fail with the old guttersnipe. "Okay, Drusilla, why did *you* get a dog kennel?" There was a smirk on Her face as she asked.

"I don't have a dog kennel, Treasure, I use an old rabbit hutch for my Smudgy. He loves the smell and it didn't cost me a penny. Saved it from the dump!"

She was silenced during which Drusilla tossed Her a scrap of hope. "If I was you, I'd leave that Chow Chow out in a rain storm with nothing but that brand new kennel to climb into."

Yes! I tail flapped enthusiastically. At long last, another human talking sense about Dog.

February: Winter Doldrums

Monday, 2nd February: *Nothing to purr about*

A freezing grey day which puts me in a black mood, as I am imprisoned with Dog who makes a ruckus every time She tries to leave It outside. Which indicates the redwood ruddy kennel is no more than a white elephant crowding my terrace although Dog's habitation of it in a rainstorm has yet to be tested.

It is now patently obvious – any gains made over Dog at Christmas have been wiped out in the face of Its losing its bits, Her ignorance of Its sly machinations and the energising effects of cold weather. Its winter wonderland is my glacial hell and I am sick of its relentless hit-and-run tactics. In addition to which it's proving impossible to see Silver Puss in addition to which Dog is targeting my squirrel when it doesn't suit me to compete for the nutcracker's hide plus I am feeling hungry all the time and find it hard to quench my thirst. On top of which I seem to be weeing constantly when the last thing I want to do is go outside into the cold. It is hard to find anything to purr about in the doldrums of winter.

Weather: fuelling Dog's power surges
Hunting prospects: dire unless I refocus on rats
Food: ravenous hunger and constant thirst are mystifying
Accommodation: improvements nixed by Dog's assaults

207

Entertainment: paws down at unlikely meetings with Silver Puss and disappearance of mice due to rats
Dog's behaviour: unacceptably squirrelous
Her training: regressed because of "poor doggy" although Its kennel rejection may provide a way back
Dogwatch: possibility of more canine asylum seekers attracted by Dog's capacity for "safe sex" (not that It's mildly interested!)

Tuesday, 3rd February: *Swift redress*

Rotten stinking fish of a day with the exception of one fine moment during the rat catcher's visit late this morning to "report on progress," or so he told Her. Fat Fiona thinks it's more likely he wanted to "get into Her knickers" as Fatty doubts he meets many other women like Her on his daily rat patrols. (Can't imagine *anyone* wanting to get into *Her* knickers; they're as holey as the Zizzz nightshirt -- have been ever since the Lying Hound exited.)

At any rate She invited the rat catcher into the office for a chat. Dog was with them. The rat catcher has been "so taken with Its teddy bear face," he brought the Chow some gravy-bone biscuits (really meant for Her). I couldn't stomach watching It smarm queen and headed for the bedroom.

GRRR-OW MAXIMUS! I was near to snoozing in my igloo when I felt the mattress sag and my eyes opened to the hot panting of Its fluffy face in mine! Dog had dared to put its front paws onto Her bed to disturb my sleep! The last thing I'd anticipated it ever doing! I instantly mega growled and spat at It before unleashing a paw swipe.

Luckily, It made a fatal error – started barking, which brought Her flying into the room, white hot with anger.

"TAMBA, GET OFF THAT BED NOW!" She bellowed and she wasn't all talk and no action. Within seconds Dog was ripped off the bed by its collar and goose stepped out of the room. A few minutes later She popped her head back in and apologetically told me "not to worry," that Dog would not bother me again but that "if nothing else, we know doggy's fully recovered."

"Took you long enough," I tail flapped back.

"Go back to sleep, Puss," She urged and then disappeared. I could hear muffled voices from the office but had no interest in them. For I realised -- Dog's latest escapade called for swift redress and my roving eyes fell upon the unused donut bed in the corner. Perfect, I decided, unexpectedly desperate for a wee.

She didn't discover the urine-soaked donut until she came to bed this evening and reeled back at the stench. Out of deference to me, She had shut Dog in the office for the night, telling It not to "even think about scratching the door." When She saw the donut bed had been fouled (by which time I was curled up in the igloo to all intents and purposes sound asleep), I heard Her mumble, "That wicked little so-and-so!" Makes my heart sing.

Wednesday, 4th February: *Branches in my backside*

A mouse pox of a day! She let yet another strange dog into my home! What the mega grrr-ow has happened to all Her House Rules??? The problem was -- She had arranged a follow-up meeting with Saffron about the creativity workshops and Saffron had to "dog sit" for a friend taken into hospital at short notice. Had to either bring the friend's beast with her or postpone the meeting. She went for the beast option, after Saffron assured Her that the dog called Skippy was "a very small, exceptionally well behaved, cat friendly Border Terrier."

So what happens? She shuts me in the bedroom, with my cat litter tray for my "convenience and comfort on a horrid cold day"! I hear Saffron arrive with the new snifter and Her tell Saffron to go into the lounge with the dogs while She "checks on Sooty who had a shock yesterday when doggy tried to jump into Pussycat's bed!" She opens the door to "check on" me. Whereupon idiot alleged owner makes fatal error -- LEAVES BEDROOM DOOR AJAR! Starts walking towards me smiling like concerned cat mum and before She can say, "What's new Pussycat?," we hear Saffron screaming "No, come back here this instant!" and within seconds see Skippy speeding through the bedroom door with Dog hot on his heels. (I learn later -- Dog bit him on the bum!)

And after that? The reputedly cat-friendly terrier high jumps onto the bed and gives me the exact same look Dog gives the Stinking Squirrel and I know beyond any doubt, as She says facing certain disaster, "Houston, we got a problem!" I don't wait to be introduced and skyrocket out of my igloo bed and over Dog's head to tear down the hallway hoping to heaven the cat flap's open. On the way I narrowly miss a head-on collision with Saffron's legs. As I scurry through the cat flap into the freezing cold, I hear two shrieking women turning "bad dogs" into "bloody" ones!

Nor does the mayhem end there! Exceptionally-badly-behaved Skippy, who's not that much larger than me, tries to slide through the cat flap. Only he gets stuck and starts squealing like a pig. She's yelling "Oh no, not again!" Saffron's hysterical that "Skippy's not my dog!" Dog tears out the back door and zooms my way when She and Saffron open it to get Skippy out. By which time my only recourse is to hot foot it up onto the pooch palace roof where Dog can't reach me and I have to camp out with conifer branches sticking into my backside until She gives me the all clear signal. No wonder I lost my appetite!

Friday, 6th February: *A flash of brilliance*

I can finally record a vastly improved state of mind after suffering through all the indignities of the past few days.

Reason No 1: She is well and truly "pissed off" with Dog and its "bum-baiting" (no doubt aggravated by Its rejection of the kennel) claiming It "summarily hijacked" Her meeting with Saffron by inciting the no-way-well-behaved Border Terrier to bolt out of the lounge and chase me until the dog unwittingly plugged himself in the cat flap. Although Skippy was eventually de-flapped, the "poor little dog" (hardly what was staring at me on the bed!) was so "hyper" afterwards that Saffron had to take him home before they'd finished their business. Result? Launch of the creativity workshops is delayed and She holds Dog responsible (MEGA MEGA PRRR!). "How can I possibly concentrate on earning money, when I've got cat-and-dog

211

fights going on daily?" She moaned to Fat Fiona recently. I don't know how Fatty replied but the simple answer in my book is, "Last in, first out!"

Reason No 2: She has reinstalled my litter tray in the hall alcove until spring so I will not have to brave the wet or cold of winter more than necessary. I am not ungrateful but She doesn't appreciate that Dog bothers me when I'm trying to wee in it and, more revolting, has made overtures to my poop.

Reason No 3: While lying on the pooch palace roof, I had a flash of brilliance -- A Superior Cat could, without any loss of face, take up residence in a dog kennel if virtually unsullied by a dog. Using a smelly old abandoned one as permanent housing is a no no. But acquiring a brand new "awfully expensive" luxury one with wall-to-wall carpeting and ornamental shrub garden, in response to an early canine rejection, is another matter entirely and, indeed, in my particular circumstances, a potential master stroke: the chance to expand my territory without a fight and to entertain Petronella when Dog is absent (There are whisperings about It going into kennels during Her holidays despite the breeder's warning against them). She will feel appreciated. Dog will appear a supremely ungrateful wretch while cat's stature will only rise in Her estimation.

Saturday, 7th February: *Gods of war smile*

Great good fortune. Today was cold but crystal clear, ideal conditions for my takeover of Dog's kennel. Her long morning walk enabled me to easily survey and settle into my new domain unchallenged. I now see the kennel's front wall and doorway will catch the sun from early morning until late afternoon. In fine weather it should warm up nicely in its nest of conifers and stay cosy for some time after the sun's gone down.

I can hop up into it with ease and the smells of newly sawn wood and rubbery carpet backing are not repulsive. A few leaves have blown inside but the floor is otherwise clean and dry. So upon entering it, I lay down in Sphinx pose facing the sunshine as it streamed through the doorway. For the first time in weeks I felt relaxed and happy knowing I could make my own Her "horribly pricey and pointless pad" for Dog.

She might easily have missed the occasion but Fate brought Her to me stomping down the back steps Dog-less, winter gardening trolley in hand. The scene set to perfection for Her discovery of my grateful occupation. Once Her eyes lit upon me, She beamed, "Hello, Pussycat, look at you!" She dropped her trolley and rushed over, wagging her tail and romping around me like an excited puppy. "Why, it's perfect for you, Sooty! " She clasped her hands together gleefully, unable to contain her rapturous joy at my presence in the pooch palace pitilessly pole axed by the presumptuous poop popper.

"You know what?" I sensed Her buzzing with fabric and furnishing ideas. "I'll put your old igloo inside so you have a nice comfy place to sleep. Along with another litter tray." She was deep in thought as She walked back towards the house. Finally looking back at me with a broad smile, "That kennel really suits you, Puss, and your old willow-pattern food bowl would look great in it, too!"

MEGA PRRR! Gods of war smiled at me today.

Sunday, 8th February: *The pooch palace is mine*

A near purr-fect day. She has unconditionally accepted my bid for the free, no-dog-attached acquisition of Its kennel. And this afternoon, made good on Her promise to install my old igloo in the pooch palace (It had been stored in the front entrance cupboard as "a spare.") What's more, She took great pains to shake it free of dust and air it in the winter sun before climbing into the kennel herself, to position it lovingly in the corner diagonally opposite the doorway so I will not have to nap in drafts. A new litter tray is definitely in the offing. "You have been weeing rather a lot lately so it might be a good idea, Puss," She confided.

I'd been sitting by the doorway supervising Her activities, disregarding most of Her prattle until She sat back on her heels and mentioned my weeing again. She patted my head as she said, "I think it's time we took a visit to the vet."

I tail flapped annoyance at the unsavoury prospect of having to see the vet about nothing more serious than ageing! Grrr-ow! I'm a cat and don't need a human telling me I'm weeing or drinking too much. It's what older cats do and my toilet habits are not Her concern. Fact is, if She'd never got Dog, my movements in and out of the house wouldn't be restricted, the litter tray wouldn't have been resurrected and She'd be none the wiser about the

214

processes of my elimination! But I decided not to get my tail in a twist; She's only human.

After a few minutes She got up off her knees and looked down at me once more. "Well, Pussycat, I wonder how doggy will react when she sees *you* in the kennel?" Her tone was conspiratorial. I think she views the upcoming event as a chance for Dog to learn the misguided human principle that it is man, and not animals, who giveth and taketh away.

Monday, 9th February: *Cats and only cats...*

One of my finest hours – consolidating my takeover of Dog's kennel, with Her assistance no less. It was another crispy blue-sky day and after breakfast She made a point of escorting Dog outside to view the error of Its rejection. This after having most gently transported me in Her arms to my new accommodation. "Here you go, Puss," She purred setting me down upon the floor at the entrance, "the perfect venue for your morning nap." And strode off for Dog.

The truly sublime fact of the confrontation was that unlike in the case of the hammock where I had to glare up at Its fuzzy face, my sitting position in Dog's kennel made It fall victim to my downward gaze. Naturally, seeing me in situ inspired Dog to push forward and wave an ugly mitt in my direction. But She checked it with the lead while I simultaneously arched into a deep and throaty growl and paw swiped the tip of Its nose. It recoiled to a respectful distance causing a sweetly vengeful expression to light up Her face before she yanked the bested beast backwards.

"Sorry, sweetheart, you had your chance," She said. Distinctly self-righteous she was and flung me a most congratulatory smile. I meowed in triumph while she gave Dog a charitable head pat. "Guess you'll have to fight Sooty for floor space now and no bets on who'll win that battle!" Her eyes conveyed a vengeful glitter as Dog sat down by her legs and cocked Its head.

Feeling the Chow's upon me, I slowly and gracefully lay down on all fours in the doorway to meditate upon the scene beneath, imagining myself the loftiest of cats guarding the valley of kings. Dog remained at heel while I, purr purr purr, I pondered on the greater truth -- *It is not humans that giveth and taketh away but cats and only cats who do.*

Tuesday, 10th February: *A new lease on life*

Ownership of the pooch palace has given me a new lease on life. Her, too. In accepting Dog's would-be digs as worthy of habitation, I have renewed Her faith in self. Which is to say, although Her decision to spend "ungodly amounts of money" on Dog's kennel was inherently flawed (Dog rejects), She is deeply satisfied with the end result (Cat accepts). Plus She has continued to improve the amenities in my new abode.

A shiny plastic litter tray arrived this afternoon, with Her hand-on-heart promise to check and, when "soiled", clean out and refill it daily with premium-quality white gravel and not ghastly grey-tinged paper-based confetti. Oh yes, and routinely air the carpeting on which it rests. The litter tray materialised on the back of my old too-good-for-the-

216

charity-shops, willow-pattern food bowl, brimming over with fresh tap water, which She delivered this morning. A long time in coming but it's out of Dog's paws now. Hence I feel quite buoyant about the way things are going.

Where is Dog in all this? – Exactly where It should be, bowing and scraping for admission repeatedly denied by my precision paw swipes.

Now that Her servicing of the kennel has been pinned down – and Dog is looking instead of touching, I can enjoy a more relaxed and peaceful life away from the two bitches. Summertime will be better yet when the palace really hots up.

Friday, 13th February: *Not over the heads of animals*

Ratty news, literally and figuratively. This morning She received a note from the rat catcher asking Her to meet up for a drink as She's the self-appointed editor of *Rat News*. *Rat News* is Her attempt to turn the progress reports into more light-hearted newsletters so She can "mend fences" with Mrs Nittypickle and be seen as "only humorously chastising residents who drag their feet on bagging the vermin." She's even penned a letter of apology to the Siamese cats. Mrs Nittypickle is thrilled.

Well, Her efforts have born unexpected fruit. *Rat News* has so impressed the local council as "a remarkable example of innovative communication encouraging good citizenship" that the rat catcher has been asked to approach Her "unofficially in the first instance" about marketing the Pest Control Department.

This evening She and Fat Fiona were in the lounge chattering about it over a bottle of wine where I had decided to join them. Dog was out of the way, on the terrace taking the cold night air. The fire was lit and as they magpied away, I was luxuriating in front of its flames, marvelling at how the winter doldrums occasioned by Dog's unprovoked assaults seemed to be behind me. Was thinking about visiting Petronella tomorrow, weather permitting, to tell her about my new "luxury" pooch palace. (In the cold harsh light of day I have to admit -- its acquisition is no mean feat for an older cat.)

Yes, I was about to turn around and curl up into a ball for a snooze when my ears pricked at Her sigh about having to take me to the vet's because I was "going through so much cat litter these days." I wouldn't have paid much attention to the remark except She added, "I've got to sort it because he'll have to go into the new cattery where doggy will be boarded when I go on holiday."

WHAT NEW CATTERY? I didn't hear another word after that. Was too shocked at mention of a "new cattery" although not enough to avoid whipping around and running over to the sofa where She was sitting. She saw me. "Oh, hi Puss, we were just talking about you!" All smiley smiley as though nothing was wrong. I pole vaulted into Her lap and dug my claws into her ample thighs. Making Her screech with pain, "OUCH, PUSSS! Why did you do *that*?" She lifted me off her lap, stood up and carried me, hind legs hanging, into the kitchen. "You'll have to go out of the room if you're gonna do that."

As I was being airlifted from the lounge, I caught Fat Fiona's eye. She cocked her head and gave me a searching look then called out after Her, "You know what they say – *never* talk over the heads of children or animals."

Too right, I tail flapped in mid air.

Saturday, 14th February: *I could spit slugs!*

Am still claw clenching over Her conversation about my having to go into kennels with Dog. She took Dog off early this morning for a "trial sleep-over" there. I could spit slugs when I think She's denying me the same courtesy. The prospect of being sent to a new cattery is maddening. Waking up today to inclement weather and buckets of rain didn't help. Another visit to Petronella scuppered. As it is, I can count the number of times I've seen Silver Puss on one paw! Does she think I've thrown her to the dogs?

How callously She removed me from the lounge yesterday! But it didn't stop me from crouching behind the door to listen in on the rest of Her conversation. I didn't catch much but enough to know the boarding kennel is located on a farm. GRRR-OW! Its cattery will undoubtedly stink of cows, horses, chickens or pigs, the accommodation will be basic in the extreme and I will have sheep dogs or German shepherds nosing around every corner. My tail whacks the hammock thinking about it!

At least I've had a Dog-free day and evening. She watched *The Godfather* as she always does when home alone feeling sorry for herself (although she's not alone, is she!). What a difficult-to-understand female She is. On the one hand She wants to be rid of the Lying Hound; yet allows him to nose back into Her life when he wishes. The shameless dog sent Her an enormous bouquet of flowers today which only made her burst into tears. Why does She cry over dead fish? To my knowledge he never rang her, certainly hasn't visited. I'd know if that chimney smoker had been in my house although he claims to have stopped. What were those flowers all about? Probably only re-marking his territory after sensing another dog in the vicinity i.e. the Precocious Brat.

Equally perplexing is Her attitude towards this "precocious brat" person. He resurfaced today as well, on the telephone, although I wasn't privy to their conversation. As the weather was so foul, I spent most of the day napping in my igloo. I only learned of his call because Zara rang Her late this afternoon to invite her to a dinner party and I was napping in my hammock by then. She volunteered that the brat had rung her, to "apologise" for not having sent Her any flowers on Valentine's Day. He'd been "away on a sales trip" without Her address to hand.

I don't know what Zara said to that but She made what seemed a most churlish remark, that She couldn't "seriously go out with a man who wears tattered jeans and a gold chain around his neck." (How can someone with holier-than-thou pyjamas criticise someone else for wearing holey jeans?)

After She hung up the phone, She swivelled round in her chair with that I'm-not-being-unreasonable-am-I expression on her face. "Maybe the Precocious Brat is a nice guy, Soot," She said leaning forward with both hands on her knees, "but would *you* go out with someone who ate his Calvin Klein underpants on a dare?"

It occurs to me now that the more relevant question which *She* should be asking herself is: *Would the Precocious Brat want to go to bed with a woman in a Zizzz nightshirt?*

Sunday, 15th February: *A most marvellous dream*

What a fabulous sleep I had! No Dog at the foot of my bed snoring or scratching itself. And I had the most marvellous dream. Woke up purring at lingering fragments of Dog's mythical escape from the boarding kennel to meet an untimely death in a field of sheep. A crusty, nearly blind old farmer had pegged It running through his fields as a mutant fox. Being Dog, It had hurled itself at the sheep and the farmer, mistaking Its rough play for a deadly assault, lifted his shotgun and in seconds blasted Dog out of my life forever.

She was devastated but only momentarily. After Its burial in the back garden with Her strewing the Lying Hound's flowers over its inert fluffy body, life returned to normal. She soon realised what a terrible burden It had been after all and knew beyond doubt that A Superior Cat is all any human needs to lead a happy and fulfilled life.

Ah well, I live in hope although my plans to visit Petronella have been sabotaged by bad weather again.

Monday, 16th February: *Reunited with Silver Puss*

A most extraordinary start to the week, when a perfect storm of events converged to reunite me with Silver Puss after weeks of wishing, wanting and worrying I'd never see her again.

This morning, when I awoke to sheets of rain pelting the bedroom window, my spirits were severely dampened. I knew Dog would be coming home later -- and after hideous weather had obliterated the potential benefits of a dogless weekend: the chance to see Petronella, invite her into the garden and show her the pooch palace without It breathing down our necks. Golden opportunities, all wiped out by torrential downpourings.

Little did I imagine another rainy day would become a precious moment in time. Nor that it would germinate from a simple act of Hers, taking a short walk down the road to post a letter. For after breakfast that is precisely what She did: threw old clothes over her pyjamas, donned her raincoat and hat and went off, leaving me sullen as a black cloud in my hammock, brooding over the cruelty of Fate.

A few minutes later She returned and directly as she stepped through the door, I knew heaven had opened up and invited me in. For there in the most unlikely of arms was my beautifully dripping wet and bedraggled Silver Puss.

"Sooty, look what I found under our camellia, of all places!" Her wonderment mirrored my own.

I leapt out of my hammock to run across not the tall grasses but the short-pile carpet of our hallway to rub noses with my sopping-wet love. Petronella had missed me as much as I her and braved the storm to catch a glimpse of her Bombay Bouncer. It was a miracle -- My Love's labour had not been lost.

Tuesday, 17th February: *A duet of meowing*

Dog's back but I continue basking in sunny memories of Petronella's surprise visit. And of how we towel and blow-dried Silver Puss back to her classic short-haired tabby self within minutes. How awesome was her transformation "from ugly duckling to catwalk queen," She'd said with undisguised admiration. "I wish I had your eyes, pussycat." With sweeter words to follow as She clicked off the dryer, "She's all yours, Soot, while I go call Fender-Bender." And the best was yet to come.

While She rang Petronella's house, I rubbed my head along pussycat's back and wrapped my tail gently around her neck. She purred with pleasure and raised her silver-grey chin into the air. Her sparkling-white whiskers twitched with contentment. Her soft purring urged me forward, to lift my paws delicately over her tail and slide myself around the other side of her elegant body. The two of us a duet of muted meowing. And so it went until She'd taken her shower and popped my courageous girl into the cat carrier to be taken home. Yes, parting was sweet sorrow but even Dog cannot dull the afterglow of that chance meeting.

Note: To Her chagrin Dog has returned from Its trial sleep-over depressed. It didn't do its usual bounce and sniff through the front door; lumbered in head low instead, bee-lining for the bedroom as though I did not exist. Perhaps the breeder is right; as a Chow It will not do well in kennels. Maybe Its woe is my good fortune -- I will not have to go into the new cattery if Dog wimps out at leaving home.

223

Thursday, 19th February: *The conundrum of Dog*

Dog remains depressed. Won't eat. Even when She put it outside in the sunny cold this morning, all It did was sag down into an uncharacteristically submissive pose on the terrace, its wrinkled nose and front paws drooping slightly over the edge. I had followed It out and seeing Dog so dejected, dropped my defensive posture and hopped into the pooch palace doorway to observe its supine body. Its tail unrolled and when I heard it sigh, I lay down like a Sphinx to seriously conjecture upon the nature of Dog. For Dog is a conundrum. A most perplexing, intricate and difficult-to-dissect problem in life.

Some humans, like the dog psychologist She derides, would type Dog as a slow-witted, ponderous and lumbering dingbat whose intelligence stands at the bottom of recognised breeds. True - It does plod, it also plops and goes down on its tummy at inopportune times, remaining there immobile, even when dragged across the floor. It has a very laid-back, placid and complacent air much of the time, except in relation to me.

It doesn't run unless pushed or inspired by the proximity of squirrels or cats. It rarely plays, except when I'm present. It's more of a bruiser than a bouncer with its own kind. Yes, Dog's a conundrum.

On the matter of sex It's allegedly female albeit without bits. But fluffy chops is no chocolate box. It may have a "teddy bear face" but that squat chunky body trots around like a baby bull in drag. More of a ball breaker than a beauty queen.

224

And yet, Dog possesses the immutable cat quality of curiosity. It stops to examine everything. Which drives Her to distraction. A five-minute walkies for Her is a day out to Dog. She tries to keep it to heel, It stops at every weed and flower. Dog sees the colours of Nature with its nose and It cannot get enough of sniffing. Dog is indeed a conundrum.

I also know – Dog is *not* obedient by nature, Dog suits Dog. An attitude to which any self-possessed cat can relate. If Dog's a star at Obedience School, it's because there's more to be gained than lost from licking the hands that feed it.

So, watching Dog down in the dumps made me wonder: Is Dog more intelligent than we know? Is It at heart a thinker, who weighs up the pros and cons of actions commanded by others? Above all else, is Dog more sensitive than we have imagined?

Dog is most certainly a conundrum. Then again, it is said that dogs resemble their owners and I know only too well, behind that authoritarian façade She is pure jellyfish. No ordinary jellyfish of course, but one who dances like a bear and stings like a bee.

Friday, 27th February: *A street-smart Smudge*

EARTH-MOVING NEWS, as She would bill it! Dog has a boyfriend, or so She would have the entire planet believe after a walk which started with "badgering from a little bugbear" (Her name for infuriating children) and ended with love at first sight (for Her anyway).

When She and Dog were in the philosophical society park this morning, She was challenged by a "too-big-for-his-boots" schoolboy who asked if She had a "proper licence" to walk Dog there. As She told Fatty this afternoon, even before she could reply, "the sanctimonious little bugbear" admonished Her "to keep It away from the flowers so it doesn't wee on them." He left Her open mouthed until She later met Drusilla who was "illegally" walking Smudge in the park. Drusilla takes the half-Tibetan spaniel there most days but refuses to pay the licence fee claiming it's "piss-poor value for money" when nearby residents constantly abuse the fully-paid-up dog walkers.

Her story of the little bugbear came as "no surprise" to Drusilla who has warned Her to watch out for the older couple who plot their morning jaunts to coincide with dog walkers' runs. The couple are retired academics who follow dog walkers along the path in the most heavily wooded areas where they hide behind trees or big shrubs so they can observe exactly where dogs defecate in order to catch their owners out for non-bagging of poops. "You have to watch your Dog's bum at all times in that park," says Drusilla.

Well, after a taxing day of listening to Her relate all this to anyone who'd listen, I thought to have an early night. But at bedtime She insisted on reviewing Dog's first meeting with Smudge – in detail. A ludicrous monologue. Dog didn't give a monkey's, remained supine on the floor at the foot of Her bed the whole time She droned on.

"Wasn't Smudgy adorable?" She oozed. "Okay, not a hunk. He's only the size of a Dachshund. Comes up to your elbows though. Beautiful red colouring and that curled up tail is the image of yours! He's got the brightest little eyes and he's very very street smart! I mean, he would be wouldn't he, living with Drusilla! C'mon now, admit it – he sniffed out that grey squirrel before you did today."

She paused for breath. Was She waiting for Dog to reply? It did – began snoring. She nattered on, unconcerned It wasn't listening: "You could do a lot worse than a Tibetan crossed with a Heinz 57. Sure, he tried to get a leg over but he can't, poor poppet. Still, he's very athletic despite his shortcomings. Look at the way he stands up like a meercat to peep over the tall grasses to see where you've gone."

Out of the blue She bolted upright in bed, clicked the bedside lamp back on. Her sudden movement startled me. I poked my head out of the igloo to see Her punch up the pillows against the bedstead. When She leaned back with arms folded, my whiskers sagged. Passion for Dog's appointed boyfriend was revving Her engines and draining my batteries.

"Smudge isn't put off by aggressive females either. Remember how you bounced him like a rubber ball, charged him like a bull and dive bombed his flank?" She leaned towards me, straining to look over the top of my igloo for a sighting of Dog. "Did he grab you by the throat, or viciously bite back? Or even snarl? He did *not*, he accepted you just the way you are!"

The intensity of her delivery grated on my nerves like a woodpecker knocking up a tree all night. I fervently yearned to wrap my tail around my ears. Better yet, Her neck. Thank goodness, She shut down for the night.

As She turned off the lamp and wriggled back down into Her bed, she couldn't resist offering the sleeping Dog one last bit of maternal advice: "Smudgy's a shrimp but he's no wimp and you should be grateful for a boyfriend who does nothing more physical than put his two front paws on your backside."

Dog's snoring was as loud as ever I'd heard it.

Saturday, 28th February: *About my drinking*

My good humour precipitated by Petronella's surprise visit is fading fast. She royally got up my nose this morning at the vet's where She did nothing but complain about my "heavy drinking." To his credit the vet was more impressed by "Mr Cat's incredible recovery [after my tree fall] without any surgical repairs."

"Pussycat's a bit thin," he told her, "but in point of fact, his leg has healed beautifully. You'd hardly know he has a limp." Sometimes the vet sees maladies that don't exist, like my "limp." But it's not the vet with whom I have a bone to pick. It's Her! For becoming hysterical about my weeing.

"Puss isn't right," She moaned to him. "He's terribly thirsty, soaks his litter tray every 48 hours. As well as the one in the dog kennel." The vet was intrigued about my peeing in Dog's kennel. What did Dog think about that, he asked, to which She replied in a truly obnoxious I'm-so-clever tone, "Actually, doggy didn't want to use it so I

228

thought it would make excellent outdoor housing for Pussycat. He's taken to it like a duck to water!"

Lies, damnable lies! Since when did *She* decide to give me the kennel? It was *I* who chose to acquire it. She merely fell into line with my decision. My tail flagellated the table as She reprised her inaccurate view of events. The vet noticed my disdain.

"Not sure you're too happy today, Mr Sooty," he said, offering a calming pat. "Let's take that blood sample so you can go home." Which he did, telling Her the results would be back in a week or so and "not to worry in the meantime" because they will probably not be "anything untoward" given my age. Why do humans insist on telling Nature what it already knows?

Yes, my happy frame of mind is disintegrating, aggravated by Dog's coming out of the dumps and shadowing my footsteps once again. She doesn't see it either, too preoccupied planning Its first birthday party, which is tantamount to a grotesque commemoration of the last day of my first year in hell!

March: A Spring of Discontent

Monday, 1st March: *Taming power of the small*

Weather*:* winter gasping with spring on the way

Hunting prospects*:* can't stop thinking about Silver Puss

Food: eating like a Fat Cat; drinking like a fish

Accommodation: upwards of 5-star in the pooch palace as long as cleaning services are up to snuff; approval of new "holiday" cattery mooted by Her is pending

Entertainment*:* hoping for more magical moments with Petronella

Dog's behaviour: growing violations of House Rule 4 prohibiting dog banging of cat

Her training*:* upturn in cat's favour due to kennel rejection

Dogwatch*:* mission critical

A snowy cold day. Had to endure one of Dog's tossing episodes while trying to relax in the pooch palace, to make the best of the sun. It was trotting about with its *I-am-the-greatest* stilted little gait. Had a dental rask bone dangling from Its mouth. Wouldn't lie down quietly and chew the thing, would it! Kept bouncing around the terrace tossing its wretched "toy" in the air. Predictably the bone hit the pooch palace wall narrowly missing my head before dropping onto the snow-covered terrace less than two feet from the doorway where I'd been sitting. Dog padded over somewhat tentatively to retrieve it.

I rose up and arched my back as my tail vibrated skyward. A warning growl made It stop and stare at me before sitting down and cocking its head in my direction. *Good,* I tail flapped, *you're listening.*

After which I shifted into a low-pitched growl and wrapped my tail around my front paws. Dog slid to the ground, never taking its slanty eyes off me. *When the student's ready, the teacher appears,* I whisker twitched.

Dog stretched its front paws forward into the snow. Its hind legs were tucked under its woolly body, making It surprisingly catlike in repose. The Chow's nose twitched with unbridled curiosity at my commanding presence and I softened my growl into a deadly purr as I sedately reclined into Sphinx pose, my eyes closing into half slits. Dog lowered its head to its paws in respectful submission.

Finally, you are learning about taming power of the small, my tail tapped on the palace floor.

Spring will come after all.

Friday, 5th March: *A hideously kinky day*

A third Day of Infamy and She has yet to inspect the damage. Dog has wrecked disaster upon me and my house after eyeing me all day long with renewed vigour. Going wherever I went, keeping just enough distance *not* to arouse Her suspicions. Sensing I was in no mood for pre-emptive strikes, It waited until She'd gone out for the evening before taking the gloves off, as She would put it. As soon as She pulled out of the drive, Dog covered me like a rash of fleas.

It pawed me in my hammock and chased me into Her bedroom where I thought to escape into the igloo. Which action unwittingly invited the woolly warmonger to hurl itself at the mattress until It managed to hoist its ungainly body up onto it. I jet propelled myself out of the igloo and fled down the hallway towards the kitchen. But with no time to circumnavigate the rubbish bin/barstool barricade, I took a sharp left into the lounge instead. It charged after me.

I jumped onto the dining table in the alcove of the bay window. Its polished surface was too slippery and I slid into Her "outrageously priced" porcelain vase of flowers propelling it forward to smash and splatter onto the floor. The crash sent me flying from the table onto the adjacent sideboard. Dog winced at the splintering but still It bounded after me. I ran at full tilt down the length of the sideboard, knocking two wine glasses over, before tripping on her silver sugar bowl which gushed a mini waterfall of white over Dog before spilling onto the carpet.

From there I leapt onto the top of the sofa. Dog followed. I fled back into the kitchen, springing up onto the counter. Dog ran in after and stood up on its hind legs trying to paw me while firing raspy barks. Which sent me in a semi-circle around the worktops until I slid into a large pan of reddish-brown mud crawling with small white worms. Except it smelled like beef and tomatoes with onion and a hint of garlic. It struck me – I was in the thick of Her Spaghetti Bolognese.

More to the point, I was out of control skidding along the greasy pan's bottom with such force that I took its sludgy contents and myself flying off the end of the counter. The pan crashed to the floor in front of the doorway to the lounge, and, plastered with its goo, I turned head over tail to land with a thud back in the other room. Temporarily stunned by the impact, I found myself lying on Her "horrendously expensive" beige carpet, unable to move and wondering why Dog did not instantly set upon me.

As I caught my breath, I saw Dog's leonine mane painted with red-brown splotches dripping tiny noodle snakes. Mercifully It cancelled the chase to hoover up the remains of Her meaty main course. For a brief instant I looked down at my own paws, no longer white but red brown and flavoured with herbs.

With Dog slurping in the soupy mire, I saw my chance to escape to the office and safe ground of Her tallest filing cabinet where I landed in a steep arch with my fur riding high on my back. I was panting profusely as my tail mega swished and one sticky spaghetti noodle rolled down my forehead to the tip of my nose. My heart thumped like a rabbit's foot and I could only gawk at the trail of reddish paw prints marking my upward progress.

I could hear Dog slurping in the kitchen, barring my exit from the house. Thus was I imprisoned in my own home -- desperately thirsty and desperate for a wee. Severely compromised and forced into the vilest of acts, to lose my honour and myself in having to behave like a dog – and indiscreetly pee. It was a hideously kinky act for which I will be wrongfully blamed.

Saturday, 6th March: *Night from hell*

It is early early morning, still dark outside and I am curled up in the pooch palace after a night in Hades. The smell of Bolognese sauce has followed me inside and my paws are a crusty brown but at least I'm away from Her screaming about the "sadistic vandalism" wrecked on our house. Her return from a very late night out, along with her faulty measures to ensure my safety, have spawned a disaster of gigantic proportion. She's even called in the Police -- well, Fat Fiona that is.

Within minutes of entering the house, She was running from room to room screaming bloody murder. Literally! In the bedroom She rang Fatty, hysterical. "Vandals have broken into the house, Fi," She shrieked, "They've tried to kill the animals. Sooty's covered in blood. Tamba too, she's lying in the bedroom, barely breathing. And there's broken glass, sick, urine and shit everywhere. Oh my gawd, what'll I do?"

I didn't wait to hear the outcome. As soon as I heard Her say Dog was near death, I shot off her swivel chair where I'd been bursting for another pee. I wanted to be spared further humiliation with a guaranteed clear run through the cat flap into the sane and less corrupt world outside.

Sunday, 7th March: *Not my fault!*

The full extent of the household damage is now being assessed by Her with the help of Fat Fiona who rushed over after the incident in response to Her frantic call. Based on what She told Her mother today, Fatty insisted

She take a tranquiliser and then after surveying the scene, talked Her through the "stark reality" of what must have happened i.e. She fell victim to a spontaneous but monumental dog-and-cat altercation. TOTALLY FALSE from my perspective!!!

The truth is – CAT fell victim to a mega squirrelous, meticulously planned and totally premeditated programme of mental abuse and physical torture which escalated out of all proportion due to Her gross negligence on matters of health and safety as should be applied to older individuals living in the presence of young rabblebowsers!

Yet, all She can think about is the "unholy mess" She has to clear up and all She can talk about is the projected battle with the insurance company over "whether a dog-and-cat spat will be viewed as an Act of God or household accident!"

She has spent the whole day cleaning up; the house reeks of disinfectant. Yesterday after lunch Dog and I were taken "in disgrace" to SnagglePets for a special offer "Wash and Blow" (two pets for the price of one). I would never have allowed this treatment had it not been for my concern about stinking of onion and garlic when visiting Petronella.

Dog didn't put up any resistance either. It's still recovering from "a severe tummy upset" with vomiting and diarrhea from "over-dosing" on Her "too spicy" Spaghetti Bolognese although the vet noted Dog's "ingestion of so much tomato content may prove a saving grace" when it comes to removing Its urine from the carpeting. Tomato juice allegedly reduces the yellow strength of a bitch's outgoings.

Today, I've had to endure a stream of snide remarks about the "widespread damage and soiling of the house" caused by OUR (in truth, Dog's!) "unforgivable behaviour." She also blames US, and all the cleaning up after US, for the recurrence of Her knee and back pain. None of which is my fault!

Monday, 8th March: *Human-gous miscarriage*

TRIPLE GRRR-OW! Dog and I must go into Dog's boarding kennel, *Noah's Ark,* late this afternoon for two days while specialists come in to "save the carpets and clean the house from top to bottom." She read us the riot act this morning, squirrelously coupling me with Dog to receive blame for everything -- although I am the injured party, battered and bruised from my tumble in the Bolognese. Plus Her catalogue of my alleged misdeeds (She read it to Her mother over the phone) is a travesty:

List of Pet Misdemeanors

1. Destruction of Ming vase (irreplaceable family heirloom)
2. Breakage of 2 wine glasses
3. Soiling of 100% New Zealand lamb's wool lounge carpet with flower-food chemicals, Bolognese sauce, granulated sugar, urine and fecal matter (latter two Dog's)
4. Watermarking of antique dining room table (Both?)

5. Soiling of kitchen carpet tiles with Bolognese sauce, urine and fecal matter (Dog only suspected)
6. Soiling of hall carpet as above (Dog and/or cat)
7. Soiling of bedroom carpet and remnant as above (Cat may be exonerated given only Dog at crime scene)
8. Soiling of bed valance with spaghetti sauce (Dog only)
9. Soiling of wall-to-wall bathroom carpeting and white throw rug with Bolognese and urine (Dog and/or cat although smaller pawprints at scene implicate cat)
10. Soiling of office carpeting, swivel chair upholstery, ottoman, desk top and (just discovered today during dusting) top of filing cabinet with Bolognese sauce and urine (Prime suspect is cat given Dog's collapse in bedroom)
11. Spoilage and/or wastage of foodstuffs including all Bolognese ingredients, sugar, flowers and flower food (Both)

She said if we were children She'd "dock our allowances for 10 years." Now She's barely uttering a civil word to me. I am utterly appalled at this human-gous miscarriage of justice.

Wednesday, 10th March: *Noah's Ark is the pits*

Noak's Ark is the pits. I am in a less than 1-star ground-floor cage on cold cement opening out onto an overgrown (full of insects and goodness knows what else) grassy area with a recycled dog bed and tatty bit of sheepskin smelling unwashed for some time. The cattery here is so big and empty you could die and no one would find your body for weeks, if ever, as the stench of your rotting carcass would be masked by the putrid pigs whose relentless oinking has kept me awake at night.

The first evening here I ran out of water and they didn't refill my bowl until late morning the next day. My litter tray is stinking. And you wouldn't feed a dog the kind of cat food they serve so I am on a hunger strike. On top of which there's no entertainment. Plus I'm sure I've heard Dog's raspy barking ever since we got here. If Its room is as ghastly as mine, I'm not surprised It returned home from its trial sleep-over in a depressed state.

Thursday, 11th March: *Back to the devils I know*

Thank goodness, that's over with and She has witnessed the "disgraceful standards of pet care" at *Noah's Ark* after sweeping into the cattery and seeing my empty water bowl, sodden litter tray and untouched "foul-looking" cat food. I was so relieved to see Her that I shelved all my anger about being sent there in the first place! At times one should be grateful for small mercies.

Within minutes Dog and I were bundled into the car and never was I more thankful to bump along in Her back seat, even with Dog panting behind me. The sweaty smell exuding from the heavily-breathing beast told me It was traumatised yet again. Perhaps the gunshots I heard on several occasions explain Dog's disquiet. If a crusty old farmer was lurking about the premises, he missed, didn't he! Yes, that was cruel. But I believe I can be forgiven in light of my unjust incarceration in *Noah's Ark* as the result of Dog's malfeasance!

I take some comfort in the fact She berated herself the whole way home. "I am so sorry, Puss," She moaned slapping the car steering wheel in a fit of self-recrimination. "I should have demanded sight of every nook and cranny of that cattery before putting you there. But I was *so* undone by the state of the house, all I could think of was getting it cleaned up."

She slapped the wheel a second time. "It never occurred to me the cattery wouldn't be as nice as the kennels. *They* are spotless, hosed down with all the bedding shaken out daily. I could eat off the floors. And the young girls there adore doggy."

A third slap broke into her wail, "So why is Tamba so distraught?" She was pleading for enlightenment but I couldn't tell Her about the gunshots. I was too sleepy until I heard Her address me directly, "Pussycat, the vet's rung me about your blood test." She paused so long that I opened my eyes and pricked my ears. "Now, it's nothing to worry about," She faltered yet again, making my whiskers twitch, "but he thinks you're diabetic."

I'm not sure what "diabetic" means but as She hasn't mentioned the "surgery" word, I am not the slightest perturbed by this news -- only glad to be back home with the devils I know, curled up in Rupert's radiator bed.

Friday, 12th March: *Circumventing Nature's way*

A long and tiring day. Made so *not* by Dog or the damp cold outside, *not* by my raging thirst, insatiable appetite or unending trips to the litter tray. No, the day seemed interminable because of Her and all Her angst . All Her upset over Dog's being in the dumps again and off its food (now hunger striking). Her being in a twist over the Ming vase being too expensive to be glued "expertly" back together, the beige carpet in the lounge being slightly lighter after cleaning and now, my diabetes.

She dragged me to the vet this morning for a thorough going over. He poked and prodded me. Felt my tummy. Listened to my heart. Examined my eyes and ears. Opened up my mouth, peeled back my lips to examine my teeth and gums. No body part untouched. All very humiliating but the vet's only human and thus forever trying to circumvent Nature's way.

He patted my head afterwards saying, "All in all, you're in amazingly good shape for a cat your age. There's no reason why we can't get this diabetes under control so you can lead a normal life."

I could have told him that. I don't fully understand this diabetes thing but I know there's nothing really amiss. For my relationship with Silver Puss is all the reassurance I need that I already lead a normal life, as long as She and Dog don't interfere with it.

After the vet helped me back into the carrier, I was quite content to rest there waiting patiently to go home. In fact, I might have nodded off had my ears not pricked at his mention of Her having to "give Pussycat two jabs of insulin daily in the scruff for the rest of his life." The thought of Her manhandling me like that every day is odious in the extreme.

"Heavens, I don't know the first thing about jabbing a cat," She'd said in a panic stricken tone I'm not thrilled to recall.

"Oh, don't worry, you'll soon learn," the vet replied. He sounded full of the joys of spring, probably delighted I'll be seeing him more often. "Nothing to it really. We always start people on oranges. A few orange jabs and you'll be ready for the real thing."

All right for *him* to say -- he's not "the real thing!"

Sunday, 14th March: *A nose out of joint*

Bugstration! It's been a most frustrating weekend of Her not letting me out of her sight. Her locking my cat flap. Keeping me imprisoned in the house, forcing me to wee in my litter tray every time I need to relieve myself. Why? So She can take me to the vet every morning and evening for insulin jabs and, under his supervision, practice on oranges to perfect Her injection technique! A preposterous waste of my time!

Added to which She's in a panic about her finances and the delayed launch of the creativity workshops to alleviate Her cash-flow problems. Added to which She's complaining about the pressures of pet parenting to anyone who'll listen. Which doesn't include Her mother who's not very sympathetic judging from what I've overheard.

When She drones on about all the problems, Her mother says things like "welcome to life at the sharp end" where you can't hide behind a desk (unless you're Dog!), or leave the job at the office or expect "the children" (us) to take themselves to the doctor (the vet) etc.

Getting no joy from Her mother, She chewed Fat Fiona's ear off this afternoon. Whinged that Her whole life is centred around Dog walking, preventing cat-and-dog fights, cleaning up after us, going to the vet, paying vet's bills, going to Obedience School, trying to find playmates for Dog. "It's no wonder I don't have any time to go out, Fi," She complained. "Now with Sooty being diabetic, I'll have to inject him twice a day. How can I possibly go on holiday? Or away for the weekend? And doggy doesn't do well in kennels!"

I get quite irritated listening to Her. Most of Her beefs are Dog related and therefore self-imposed. Yet She talks as if I'm a burden when for years She praised me for being "low maintenance," "no trouble at all" and "good value for money." She's never paid for expensive pet insurance or costly trips to the vet for me! It's not my fault She opted to get a squirrelous dog or that She and the vet have chosen to treat me as diabetic.

In sum my nose is out of joint. At least Dog 's not in my face -- It's suffering from some kind of adverse reaction to being at *Noah's Ark*. It's subdued, won't eat. She's asked the vet if he knows any pet psychiatrists or if there's such a thing as a *dog whisperer*. Saffron, who believes in reincarnation, has theorised that Dog may have been "severely maimed in a previous life" and *Noah's Ark* has triggered Its "cellular memory" of the event which is now stuck in Dog's psyche and in need of expunging.

Suggesting to me that Dog needs an Exorcist, not a Whisperer!

Saturday, 20th March: *Greater good fortune*

It's the first day of Spring and after a week of being jabbed in the scruff, I feel like a porcupine with its quills knocked in. However, I have to admit -- insulin injections have become an inconsequential part of my daily routine. She puts me up on the kitchen counter, serves me a meal and while my nose is deeply embedded in the bowl, She's in and out with the jab in seconds in order that I become "a new cat within weeks."

The first time she injected me on her own, She made a point of talking up all the benefits: "You won't have to wee as much, Puss (meaning She won't have to clean my litter tray as frequently); you'll not be nearly so thirsty (She won't have to fill my water bowl as often); and you won't be so hungry all the time (She'll save money on food)."

"Yes, Soot," She said, "this feline diabetes management may cost a bundle, but you're worth it!" Which is Her typically squirrelous way of positioning something unpleasant as beneficial to me when in fact it's all about making Her life easier! On the plus side, now that I've been branded "a diabetic cat," She is spending more time (even more than after my tree fall) "honouring my needs" --

- Serving meals earlier and on a tighter schedule (instead of whenever it suits Her) due to insulin injection requirements

244

- Paying more attention to my dietary requirements generally
- Providing me with higher-quality cat food
- More frequent brushing and grooming (after vet's comment on "poor condition of coat" extending Her *Noah's Ark* guilt trip)
- Delivering better cleaning services in relation to my igloo bed, my hammock and the pooch palace
- Closer scrutiny of Dog's behaviour to ensure diabetic cat's improved health and wellbeing and better yet,
- Arranging Her social life, comings and goings, holiday plans etc around my requirements. (As for holidays I am supremely confident of a return to *The Cat's Whiskers* now that down-market voyages on *Noah's Ark* are out of the question.)

In short, I shall have transformed the human judgment of ill being into A Superior Cat's greater good fortune. I must tell Petronella the good news.

Sunday, 21st March: *Times that try dogs' souls*

I had rather an amusing day despite my failure to see Silver Puss whose house had that abandoned look of owners gone on holiday when I popped in. On my way back down the road, I saw Cowboy Bebop with his nose in a bush and no Mrs Houndslow. Before I could think how to avoid him, he picked up my scent and set off towards me with unmistakeable intent.

I turned tail and ran back towards Petronella's house, sure my best escape route would be up the tree next to

Fender-Bender's front wall, which was exactly the route I took. Luckily, I made it but the predatory cow dog started running back and forth along the bottom barking up a frenzy while trying to spring up the wall to get at me.

At first I thought to skitter to the back of Fender-Bender's house and take the garden route home. Then it dawned on me – I could simply saunter back and forth along the wall in front of the cow dog to incite more barking and flush Mrs Houndslow out of her house, assuming she was home. I decided to try it.

Aside from the unpleasant racket I quite enjoyed encouraging the pig-tail pooch to heave himself up the wall and tumble backwards repeatedly. His barking got louder and more insistent. I sat down and waved my tail at him.

After awhile a small van pulled up in front of Fender-Bender's house. A short rotund man got out of it, carrying something resembling a fishing net. He started creeping towards Bebop who was so wound up by my presence out of his reach that the cow dog didn't notice the figure stealing up behind. All of a sudden, the man threw the net over Bebop, there was a tussle which made Bebop bewildered and enabled the man to bundle the squat podger into his van and drive off.

"Magic," I purred. After they'd gone, I sat atop the mountain of my wall a little longer to savour the view of our road made peaceful once again as giving each paw a lick, I was grateful for the catalytical times that try dogs' souls.

Monday, 22nd March: *Landing my fish*

Dog's depression has lifted. Its appetite is back. So are Its evil ways proven by its wanton destruction of the flying fish on my carpet cat scratching post today! Said post has been located in a corner of Her office since Christmas. In theory, to provide me with chances to use it under Her supervision so Dog cannot abuse me in the process. Prior to today the scratching post has sat there with the fish lying suspended from its top by a string. Until this morning that is, when She went out to the kitchen and Dog got up and trundled over to it as I watched from the hammock.

I stood up as soon as It went on the move. Whereupon It cast a furtive glance in my direction. I arched my back. It looked away then raised one belligerent paw to bat my fish into flight. Before I could protest, It caught the fish in its teeth and viciously pulled it off the string. Seconds later Dog was dancing around the office, shaking the fish in its mouth before – yes, It couldn't help itself – tossing the fish over head to hit the door of the cupboard behind the post.

My fish dropped to the floor. Dog ambled over to sniff it, pawed it once then lost interest and trotted out of the room. A few moments later She came back into the office, took one look at the dead fish, another at me and said, "Oh Pussycat, you're supposed to play with it, not fillet it!" Which remark She thought terribly funny as She was giggling the whole time she stooped down to pick my fish off the floor. "How on earth did you manage that, Soot?"

She dangled it in front of me. I'd have paw swatted Her had I not been so disgusted. It never occurred to Her that

247

it was Dog who landed my fish, not even when It casually strolled back into the office to nose around my post.

Dog's a conniving bitch and still, She doesn't see it!

Wednesday, 24th March: *Tasteless food foist on me*

Now tasteless diabetic cat food is being foist upon me! A supposedly chickeny concoction I refuse to eat which is sending Her into a tiz. She daren't jab me on an empty stomach as I may go into "insulin shock" which terrifies Her! "Pussycat, what *am* I going to do with you?" She whined at me this morning after I took one bite and turned my nose up at the rest. "This is especially for pets with your condition. Please eat it. It's not cheap, you know!"

She couldn't avoid the cost mention, could she! Which made it all the more pleasurable to reject the bland fare. Forcing Her to feed me Dog's natural nutrition fresh tripe mix instead. Offally delicious, it was too. I ate every bite and could easily have downed more.

"Glad you're eating *something*," She said a trifle snippily while giving me my morning jab on the kitchen counter. Not wanting to throw my food out, She tried it on Dog. "What do *you* think of the diabetic cat food?" She put my bowl down on the floor and Dog scoffed the lot. "That's convenient -- at least it won't go to waste." She dripped rather more sarcasm than was called for. "What a household, dogs eating diabetic cat food and diabetic cats eating dog food!"

All in all, She was exceptionally disagreeable. Which I put down to the self-created pressure of planning Dog's birthday party. Out of deference to my new "diabetic cat" status, She's not inviting any other dogs -- only Rupert, three neighbourhood children and one mum. The whole enterprise smacks of *Alice in Wonderland*. There'll be a Mad Hatter and Cheshire Cat coming before long!

As for Dog's de-fishing of my scratching post, She has promised to re-attach the fish when She "gets a minute." Which suggests my post will be "under repair" for the next three years, like our old doorbell.

<u>Friday, 26th March</u>: *Enter the Precocious Brat*

Strange goings on. Which started late this morning, when She was in the kitchen making a cheese-and-sausage birthday cake for Dog's party tomorrow. Her portable phone rang. She answered it and blushed, "Oh, hello, it's been awhile, hasn't it?" Then turned her back on me and walked out of the room, leaving Dog's unmade cake on the counter with It sniffing like a Bloodhound below.

Being a diabetic cat with a voracious appetite, I deemed it quite fitting to walk across the counter to remove a few cheesy chunks as retribution for Its illegal procurement of my fish! I managed three before She set upon my back with an angry, "SOOTY, bad cat!" In other circumstances I'd have been seriously affronted. But given Her insecure state over Dog's party, I forgave her lifting me up by the scruff and plonking me back down on the other side of the sink.

"Right, you two, outside!" She wasn't angry, though. More like panicked -- began rushing around the kitchen; threw the unfinished cake into the fridge, slung all the dirty dishes and mugs into the sink. "Lord, he'll be here in half an hour and this place is a tip," She groaned at me.

The word "he" set my tail lashing at the prospect of the Lying Hound skulking back into our lives. She failed to notice my dismay, opened the back door to corral us out. Then grabbed a dental rask bone out of the cupboard and threw it onto the terrace. Dog chased after it. "Okay, Soot," She said hurriedly carrying me down the back steps to the pooch palace roof. "Here you go, Pussycat, take a sunbath." She gave me a fleeting pat and flew back through the door, shutting it behind her.

I was so taken aback by Her frantic behaviour I just sat there, wondering what on earth was going on. Decided to investigate. Dog was bone tossing at the bottom of the garden so I was able to scamper back over to my cat flap unchallenged. But when I got there, it wouldn't budge even with my entire body pressing against it. I was shocked to the core. In all my years with Her I have never before been subjected to a lock-out!

I lay down and must have been snoozing as the ring of the door chimes startled me. I went onto high alert, scanning the garden for Dog. It was lying down near the bottom fence chewing its bone. I peered through the dusty plastic of the cat flap and saw Her go to the front door. She'd exchanged her wrinkled dog-walker's track suit for a skirt and blouse, a rarity these days.

When She opened the door, there stood a solidly built, youngish man (not the Lying Hound) in its frame. Wearing some kind of jacket over a pair of slightly tattered jeans. She leaned forward, gave him a peck on the cheek as he entered. He turned back towards Her and I could see from his profile that he wasn't much taller than she was. She closed the door and turned to face him. He took a step towards her, then reached out to envelop Her in the biggest bear hug I've ever seen her receive. A male embrace exceptionally singular, beyond even powers of A.S. Cat to define. The youngish man did not kiss Her; he only hugged her with a limitless depth of liking She did not resist. She'd told me nothing but I knew -- the Precocious Brat had come.

Saturday, 27th March: *No celebration for me!*

I am no wiser about the strange goings on of yesterday. The young man (Surely the Precocious Brat!) blew in and out of our house like a warm breeze. One bear hug upon entry, a disappearance in the vicinity of Her office and a short time later, gone with the wind. More than that, I do not know and so far She's made no mention of his visit to me or anyone else I'm aware of. Most unlike Her.

On the back of these strange goings on, the not-eagerly-awaited birthday party came and went this afternoon. As dogless parties for a dog go, it might have been barely tolerable had it not been for Her unpardonable oversight. She neglected to give cat a single piece of Dog's cheese-and-sausage birthday cake despite giving some to everyone else. Not one morsel came my way – despite my lying quietly and politely on the sofa the entire time, attending an event which is absolutely no cause for personal celebration!

April: Have Patience and Endure

Saturday, 3rd April: *A palace intruder*

More bugstration! No sight of Petronella. Went over to Fender-Bender's early this morning and found the house and garden totally deserted. *Where* is Silver Puss? My efforts to see her came to nothing. Returned home intending to console myself by spending a sunny afternoon in the pooch palace (She and Dog have gone to Saffron's for another creativity workshops meeting) and made an ugly discovery. Some arrogant and filthy creature has entered my abode and pooped in the corner directly opposite the igloo bed. The sluggy-looking black pellets stink.

My immediate thought was to brand Dog the culprit. But Dog hates the pooch palace, won't go near it and the poop doesn't in fact look or smell like Dog's. It's definitely too large for a rabbit's and smaller than a deer's. Plus the crusty-black feces contain seeds, a telltale sign of berries, and berries usually mean foxes who're no better than dog vermin. How dare one come into *my* pooch palace! Knowing Her, this mess won't get cleaned up for days and She'll think it's *mine*! Grrr-ow! How can truth out in light of Her ignorance? Ah well, hope springs eternal so I shall settle for stretching out across the warm stones of my terrace as I hope for -

Weather: an inordinately hot month to set Dog panting amongst the shrubs *before* summer begins

Hunting prospects: new chances to fell the Stinking Squirrel (I feel infinitely more energetic these days!)

Food: an end to the diabetic stuff

Accommodation: a new igloo for the bedroom

Entertainment: seeing Petronella more often and Her and Dog less

Dog's behaviour: collaboration for mutual gain (if cat thinks laterally)?

Her training: advancement by cat's pressing of diabetic status to fullest advantage

Dogwatch: no new ones on the road (Are rumours of foxes trying to move in from London boroughs true?)

Sunday, 4th April: *Love's gentle spring*

Wonderful news! Silver Puss is back. I went over to Fender-Bender's this morning and found her on the shed roof, grooming herself to sleek perfection. I rushed forward along the wall to join her, unable to suppress an ecstatic meow. Petronella's head shot up and when she spotted my stalking body, she scurried across the roof to greet me. As I approached, she jumped up on her strong back legs to place her luscious tabby paws on top of the wall, tilting her exquisitely furry face upwards towards mine. Seconds later our noses touched. And I could only marvel at how love's gentle spring always fresh remains. Better yet, pussycat is free of the wearisome Westies -- Fender-Bender's parents have returned from their cruise and Mangle and Wurzel are gone, which augurs well for our future.

Would that She was so blessed. I returned home in the late afternoon to a bad smell. As soon as I entered the house, I knew the Lying Hound had been there; his stale nicotine odour clung to the air. I found Her in the lounge, draped over the sofa, staring disconsolately at the ceiling. She was clasping a cushion to her breast, her face was pale and drawn. If She knew how old and haggard such pained expressions made her, she'd never be upset again. But She is not yet so enlightened and barely squeaked out a feeble "Hi, Puss" when she saw me come into the room.

I purred unsympathetically. For it's obvious -- the drama of her failed love affair is playing out its last scene and it's dragging on far too long! Dog who ventured in behind me sensed the sorrowful atmosphere and absolved itself of any responsibility by running off, leaving *me* to sort out Her sorry situation.

I don't need to be told what went on. It's patently obvious – the Lying Hound dropped in and nothing's changed. He only came back to spy upon Her like an untimely frost, not out of genuine concern but because he sniffs a new dog hunting on what he erroneously regards as his territory. When will She learn?

Note: Victory! Today She returned what's left of the diabetic cat food to the vet ("too expensive for the little…") and has given into my demands for tastier victuals. I am now being fed premier-quality cat food "for seniors." Took Her long enough!

Tuesday, 6th April: *She's finally getting it*

More ado about nothing. Dog completed *Pooch Perfect's* Level 1 Obedience Training Course this evening. On Her fourth attempt, I hasten to add. As has been the case on and off for the past year, She took It off to class after dinner (mine anyway; Dog had to go hungry before class). Only this time She returned waving a ribbon in my face. "Look, Soot, we did it!" She was all waggy tails. "Doggy's passed. Did everything right first time. She got a *Good Citizen* certificate tonight!"

You mean, YOU finally got it right, I whisker twitched at Her, recalling what Miss Dawgsbody had said about Dog's resistance to learning. If nothing else, Its "graduation" has wiped away some of Her upset at yesterday's visit from the Lying Hound. But while She's deliriously happy about the Chow's achievement, Dog seems not to give a damn. It sauntered down the hallway into the kitchen to slurp up water from its bowl without a tail quiver. Its attitude remains impenetrable.

I cannot but wonder what it would take for Dog to be impressed by Her. I know It's impressed by me -- even if It doesn't always take heed of my instruction.

Thursday, 8th April: *Dog does a "Ripper"*

Dog's "good citizen" award is a joke after what It did today. She and Fat Fiona took It for a late afternoon walk in the philosophical park and upon returning were in the drive talking when Dog bolted, practically pulling Her over before she let go of its lead. It was chasing after a neighbour's long-haired Persian cross called Hedge. Scared the cat up a tree in the garden of a house at the bottom of our road. Dog whipped the lead's hard plastic reel head around with such force that the Chow appears to have done "a Jack the Ripper" on a neighbour's "possibly-priceless-family-heirloom" plant pot. Knowing the owners were away, She ran into the garden after Dog where she discovered the vertically severed stone pot with "gutted" geranium wilting on the pathway.

She and Fatty spent most of the evening dissecting every aspect of the incident given She did not actually see Dog bump off the pot and only surmises Its the culprit. I refused to listen to all their conjecture. As a cat who's had to cohabit with Dog for the past year, I don't doubt the guilty party or that Its "obedience school" achievement is thinly veiled squirrelousness at best.

The good news is – She's arranged to take Dog on a so-called "bonding holiday" at a dog-friendly hotel in Cornwall for five days from Saturday and "Dearest Pussycat" will be going to *The Cat's Whiskers*. Prrr! Prrr! She is back on track with my holiday accommodation although it will cost Her more now as diabetic cat care is extra. But that's Her problem.

Wednesday, 14th April: *Disaster in Paradise*

I am home after a delightful stay at *The Cat's Whiskers*. The food was excellent, my jabs were painless and on time and my water bowl and litter tray were checked twice a day. As usual the entertainment was scintillating although things got out of hand momentarily when the rabbit Piggle was set upon by the corpulent orange tabby who escaped from the cage next to mine. It was all very exciting although Piggle didn't think so.

By comparison Her "bonding holiday" with Dog was "an unmitigated disaster." I heard Her telling Fatty about it on hands-free this evening. She's so stressed with back and neck pain, she can't hold a phone up to her ear for very long. I listened to Her litany of woes from the hammock. Dog had retired to the bedroom early, not having eaten Its dinner once again. For all It appears tough and independent, Dog doesn't like leaving home. She said It ate no food except for Her "leftovers," like the sausages from the English cooked breakfasts she was served.

She and Dog stayed at a hotel called *Poochini's Paradise*, run by two former advertising executives and dog lovers, Edward and Raymond, whom She says are "gay as a couple of Mexican tablecloths." The men make a habit of rescuing Great Danes and currently have two, Starsky and Hutch, in addition to a 13-year-old mongrel whom they recently renamed Alzhi after the dog started "going bananas every day at sundown chasing imaginary cats off the premises."

Every night after dinner Edward and Raymond brought their horse-size Danes into the hotel lounge to join the guests and their dogs for coffee, biscuits (each dog being entitled to three) and liqueurs (owners only). The Danes preferred sitting in their owners' laps to lying on the floor. "Sounds like a madhouse to me," I heard Fatty say.

She said not, that all the dogs "got on famously and stayed out of trouble" except for one greyhound called

Slick Willy who chased a pheasant over a cliff while they were there.

"Goodness, did the dog survive?" Fatty asked in wonder.

"Oh yes," She said, "it was rescued by an RAF helicopter." Apparently, the greyhound fell into the branches of a tree growing out of the cliff side and had enough sense not to move.

"Was it badly hurt?" Fatty queried.

"Oh no," She told her, "it only suffered a few scratches but was so terrified it peed and pooped all over the rescue team coming up from underneath the tree in case it should fall out."

Ironically, it was the bird who came unstuck in the end: knocked itself out on a rock and fell off the cliff, She said.

They chattered on during which She admitted that Dog "didn't settle" the whole time they were there. The Chow refused to eat until She began sharing Her meals with It.

What a masterful manipulator is Dog. Dog barks, She listens. Dog hunger strikes, She starves. Dog behaves like a dog, She jumps. Was Dog a cat in a previous life?

Friday, 16th April: *The badgers are coming!*

The stress of dealing with Dog is definitely getting to Her. She awoke early this morning screaming, "The badgers are coming, the badgers are coming!" Was kicking the mattress with both legs to the point where my igloo bed was rocking. I jumped out, wondering if we were having an earthquake until I realised it was only Her wrestling with invisible badgers.

Then Her flailing stopped, She woke up and poured out a minute-by-minute description of being attacked by gorilla-size badgers in the home of one of Fat Fiona's friends "who was wearing yellow rubber gloves to her elbows."

I couldn't think of a thing to say about Her vivid imaginings of being devoured by mythical badgers. The simple response would have been, "It's all in your mind," without adding it would be horrifying being in Hers. It's not surprising She's started a meditation course with Saffron "to deal with stress on the Home Front." Claims Her back can't take the yoga. Yawn!

Saturday, 17th April: *Zero tolerance*

Marvelous sunny day. Spent most of it with Petronella in her garden. Fender-Bender was outside pruning shrubs. She came over to greet me after I jumped down from the wall onto the shed roof to sit beside Silver Puss who'd been lying there like a Sphinx. "So, it's more than just sex in the city, is it, Sooty?" She looked up at me and grinned. If Fender-Bender were a cat, she'd be a luscious short-haired tabby rolling around in clotted cream. Petronella stirred herself to walk around me purring.

I returned home in a brilliant mood to find Her angsting in the kitchen with Fat Fiona who was perched on one of our stools sipping coffee while She was moaning over dishes in the sink. Too engrossed in chatting, they didn't notice my arrival. The first thing I heard Her say was, "He says he's changed." My tail flapped on the carpet at mention of the perfidious "he."

"Stopped smoking you mean?" Fatty couldn't hide her sarcasm. She wasn't fooled either.

"So he says." *His lies smell*, I would have told Her.

"I think he's a time waster." Fatty never minces words.

"You sound like Zara." She mimicked Zara's studied cut-glass accent, "Dahhhling, he's not even *window* shopping material!" They both laughed.

"What about the Precocious Brat person? You never mention him." This time I could see Fatty's tongue hanging out.

She kept her head down in the sink: "Nothing much to tell, he's all over the place working plus we're a total mismatch." *Untrue, you're a Lying Hound too – The Brat wears holey jeans and you wear holey pyjamas,* my whiskers twitched.

"Pity," Fatty sighed, "I rather liked the sound of him."

All She said to that was "Hmm" and changed the subject. "Anyway, no time for men, Fi. Keeping the animals going and touting for new business is more than enough on my plate."

"No excuse," said Fatty refusing to bow to Her self pity, "Millions of working people have pets and partners."

"Sure, but not a diabetic cat and dog with osteoarthritis, fireworks dementia and eating disorders who needs a psychoanalyst." Her brow was seriously wrinkled.

Fiona couldn't help herself: "Look at the mother!"

"FIONA! That was cruel in the extreme!" She screeched, Fatty's attempts at humour ignored. "You don't know what it's like being on an endless treadmill of walkies, housecleaning, vet's visits, dog-and-cat skirmishes, poop removal, insulin jabs, you name it. I'm even having nightmares about gigantic badgers!" She was near frothing at the mouth until she stopped and looked at Fiona for a drop of sympathy. Fatty wasn't doling out any today.

"This isn't about the pets," she said professorially. "It's about you and *family* instead of you and *work*!"

"Oh gawd," She blustered, "you sound just like Mum."

Fatty was treating Her with zero tolerance: "Be honest, until the dog arrived and Sooty became diabetic, a pet to you was an accessory, nice to have in the wardrobe between business trips but *please*, don't expect me to wash out the stains and iron out the wrinkles every week."

"Fi!" This time She piglet squealed. "What a terrible thing to say. You make me sound like Cruella DeVille!"

Their conversation was crackling but by that time I was bored and departed for the pooch palace to ruminate upon Fatty's central theme – that in essence we pets are cutting Her executive self down to size. High time, too!

Monday, 19th April: *MORE bum baiting?*

UPROAR! Dog's been accused of "viciously assaulting" the postman -- this morning, when It was outside the house on its extendible lead locked on a measured length and threaded under the front door so It could be, She said, "truly fulfilled like Its ancestors when guarding monasteries of Tibetan monks." How She connected our home with a monastery is beyond me. She's no monk. But somehow she's convinced Dog will be a "healthier and less fretful canine" (thus its appetite will improve) if It has a proper job i.e. protecting our entrance under Her management. So after walkies and since the weather was mild, She put Dog "out to work" -- figuring It couldn't get into any trouble as she can see most of Its movements from the office window. The fact Her head's always buried in a computer was overlooked.

Just as I was drifting off to sleep in my hammock, I was woken out of my torpor by Dog's staccato barking and a loud banging on the office window. It was the postie yelling at Her to "remove the attack dog immediately," in response to which She tore out of the office like a whippet with me hot on her tail and flung the door open with Dog's lead gripped tightly in Her hand. It was barking up a storm amid the seething postie's scolding that She had "no business impeding delivery of the mail." Which accusation She met with a vigorous denial.

"That's ridiculous, she was only barking," She insisted. Mind you, She had a job trying to restrain Dog from rushing at the man. In the postie's defence the Chow was not behaving like a cuddly soft toy.

"You call biting my bum 'barking'?" The postie was red-faced as he pointed at his backside.

"Biting your bum? No way! Doggy's never even snapped at anyone!" She was outraged as she yanked Dog backwards.

"Are you calling me a liar?" The man gave her a filthy look.

"I'm saying my dog wouldn't bite anyone on the bum!" Her tone had become marginally less strident and I wondered -- had the same Border Terrier crossing my mind run into Hers?

The postie looked murderous. "I'll report you next time," he threatened before turning on his heel and striding off in a huff.

"Rubbish!" She spat under her breath although heavy breathing said she was unnerved. After pulling Dog back inside and closing the door, she got down on her knees and grasped Its woolly head in both hands and shook it from side to side. "You didn't bite that pissy little postie on his bastardly little bum, did you, pupsydoodle?" It was a definite question albeit softly uttered.

Dog cast its head downward and said nothing. Did It in fact view the postie as bum bait? We'll never know; however, Dog's out of work after only one day.

Wednesday, 21st April: *Bitch of a thousand bitches*
Dog's bugstration at losing Its first job has caused It to ferociously attack the mail, as witnessed by me from the hammock. It happened this morning when the postie whom She's avoiding like rabies began popping items through the letterbox. At the whoosh of initial droppings, Dog rushed towards the door barking with seemingly pent-pent-up rage. As more post showered down, Dog leapt up at it like a killer shark snapping its jaws at a bait ball of tiny white fish.

At that point She came running out of the office yelling, "What the hell's going on?" Dog's barking, the click of the mail flap followed by the mysterious ripping of paper had raised alarm bells. "Oh, bitch of a thousand bitches, what have you done?" She was incandescent, shrieking as she dropped to her knees and began crawling across the floor to examine the damage while Dog unfazed nonchalantly sniffed at its handiwork. Within seconds She descended into fits of cursing. "Oh, shit!" She spat out first. "Double shit!" She added, ultimately screaming, "Shit of a thousand shits!" I could see She was trying to reassemble several pieces of paper into a recognisable whole.

When she couldn't solve the puzzle of Dog's shreddings, She scooped up the mess of bits with one hand, grabbed Dog's collar with the other and yanked It down to face her on the floor. "Do you know what this is, you red ruddy toerag? She glowered as she shoved the fistful into Dog's impassive face. "This is a cheque from my biggest client, only now it's not a cheque, it's a Caesar salad!" She threw the "salad" at Dog who jerked itself out of Her grasp and ran off to head butt its way out the back door. She was left behind kneeling with closed eyes and both fists raised to heaven.

Fortunately, She has a meditation session tonight.

Thursday, 22nd April: *Totally off Her trolley*

Our alleged owner has finally gone off her trolley. I've always known She was eccentric. Not the reserved, tattily-dressed intellectual type but an in-your-face, coming-to-a-cinema-near-you, Shakespeare-ignorant sort. And today She absolutely beyond any shadow lost the plot – with Dog close behind!

It all started with Her dropping Dog's Toy Box on the bedroom floor in front of the Chow's nose. Thud! Followed by Her snarling, "You WILL play with me!" Then Her going down onto all fours and head butting Dog who, totally taken by surprise, got up and ran out of the room. Prompting Her to run after It while chucking an armful of toys at it, one by one. All the while She was barking. I mean, deep-throated GURR barking the whole time, pretending to pant like a dog with Her tongue hanging out!

After some chasing around, I think Dog began to see Her as one of them. It started doing its bully-girl wriggle and dive bombing Her. She squeaked a squidgy spidery-looking thing at It and Dog charged. Whereupon She turned tail and ran out the back door down the steps to the terrace with Dog in hot pursuit and me watching from the kitchen window.

She ran in circles around the garden table with Dog chasing behind. Until It stopped and ran back into the kitchen and She chased after Dog. It went on like this, in and out of the house, until She collapsed laughing hysterically in a heap in the hallway and Dog slid into a panting spread-eagled halt on the terrace with Its bum to us.

Eventually She picked herself off the floor and giggled her way into the office where She rang Saffron. From snatches of their conversation, I gather Saffron had advised Her to "get down and dirty" with Dog as a form of "laughter therapy" to help Her bond better with the Chow while "de-stressing" about Its mastication of Her cheque. I must confess – She's in a far better mood. Didn't slip in any Bolognese either.

Friday, 23rd April: *Navels are ugly*

What a refreshing change! She woke up on top of the world this morning. Bounced out of bed calling me "a precocious puss." Gave the "toerag" a hug. All her anger at the shredded cheque seems to have drowned in the wake of yesterday's "laughter therapy." Even Her backache has "miraculously disappeared," She told her mother. I don't know how laughter therapy works but I suppose it takes people's minds off examining their navels, which must be good -- navels are ugly.

Saturday, 24th April: *She protests too much*

Grrr-ow! A horrid day with an elephant grey sky and rain forest outbursts. Far too wet to visit Petronella. Too soggy to go out for any wees making the litter tray an imperative. I don't much like using it in warm weather. It becomes unpleasantly sharp too quickly despite the pristine white gravel She puts in it and Her efforts to rake up every poop immediately now that I'm a diabetic cat. At least I didn't have to go out for walkies like Her and Dog. They looked wet and damp all day long.

This evening She snuck out to see The Brat and I think she's blown it with him. Went out after dinner, thankfully shut Dog in the office to avoid another "Bolognese Brouhaha."

Per usual these days She didn't tell me where she was going. Saw She wasn't "dressed up posh" or in the dog-walking garb she often puts on to visit Fatty or other friends. Curious! She was wearing a salmon-coloured jacket over denim jeans. Normally She wouldn't be caught dead in jeans outside the house. Says they're strictly for "20-somethings and beautiful people," neither of which She is! Like Dog, She's a conundrum.

I don't know how long She was gone as I'd fallen asleep in my igloo until I heard the front door open. She was unusually quiet entering the house. No "Hey, everyone, I'm home!" which since Dog's arrival has become Her standard greeting. In fact, I'd have thought Her a stranger had I not smelled her fresh scent. She silently escorted Dog out for its last wee of the night, came into the bedroom a few minutes later with It padding behind. Put Her handbag on the dressing table and sat down on the bed within petting distance of my igloo.

"Hi, Puss," She said softly. There was an uncharacteristic air of resignation about her which drew me out of the igloo and into her lap where She stroked me thoughtfully from head to tail. She was silent. I began to purr, which was Her signal to begin. She heaved a long sigh, "He wasn't right for me anyway. We have absolutely nothing in common. He's far too impatient, says he knows what he wants and that it's me who's stuck. Wants me to decide although I hardly know him."

She was picking up the pace of her thoughtful stroking. "Actually, he excells in making waves." Her air of resignation was turning indignant.

"Do you know what he told me? That he went golfing on this very exclusive course wearing a baseball cap backwards to deliberately irritate the 'old wankers trying to ram an outdated dress code down younger members' throats.' The guy's a rebel. Do I need such a person in my life?"

Her stroking went up a gear to vigorous patting and I prepared to dig my claws in if She got out of hand. Which She did but I couldn't claw her because she whisked me up by the armpits to look me in the eye. "I mean really, Puss, can you in your wildest nightmares imagine me with a precocious brat like that?" She angrily shook my body in Her face. "It's not me, is it!"

With a final "harrumph" She nearly threw me back into the igloo where I sat growling softly, "The alleged owner protests way too much."

Sunday, 25th April: *A pale outrider on the fence*

A vile day when Nature in the raw cast a grey shadow across our garden like the grimmest of reapers. When family and friends fell prey to a verminous intruder. Creating mayhem amongst the shrubs and, thankfully, an unexpected heroine.

I should have detected the signs early on. Dog did. It had been an uneasy night following Her outburst of cat shaking. After She'd finally gone to bed and the house was quiet, I felt the crackle of silent electricity in the air, the unease of a night on the edge of thunder and lightning. Later on as She slept, Dog woke me up with restless panting. It too was unsettled by the gathering storm until the heavens opened and rain brought blessed relief and Dog and I slept once again although She'd never stirred.

By early morning a muted sun had broken through the clouds but Dog was fitful once more. She too heard Its unease. "Need to go out, Tamba?" She asked sleepily hoisting herself out of bed. She sloped off to open the back door but Dog wouldn't go out, a reluctance I should have registered. She returned to bed.

I went back to sleep until awoken by an insatiable desire to wee. I crept to the edge of the bed and seeing Dog asleep, went out onto the terrace. There, I saw a reddish sky, a harbinger of the chaos to come. The grass was wet and warmish so after weeing I hopped up into the pooch palace to observe unfolding of the day until my nose and ears told me of another's presence. It was not a vile discovery but the music of a familiar yet too harsh meow coming from the foot of my garden. I jumped down onto the terrace to survey the bottom fence and there atop it was my resplendent Silver Puss.

I didn't think to scan the horizon for any others who might be lurking, couldn't wait to shoot down the stone steps to greet Petronella. Out of the corner of my eye I saw her leap down into the garden – and that's when it all began. The fatal signs had been there all along. More slug-like seedy poops on the grass between us and more abhorrent -- the glassy-eyed Stinking Squirrel lying on its back in frozen death. And what I didn't catch in time – the wounded cub panting beneath the taller conifer.

Petronella veered off towards the tree but not before I'd seen reckless abandon turn her eyes to jaundiced green. I smelled the stink of terror but it was not hers until another's presence loomed large above us. A pale outrider upon the fence, a gaunt and scruffy vixen going hairless except for stark grey patches of furry tufts about her shoulders and flank. Her bared teeth and shark's eyes looked from Petronella to the conifer and there, the hapless cub whom

I knew with sinking heart would plunge us all into the valley of the shadow, lambs before the slaughter of a territorial imperative.

The fox dived off the fence and caught Silver Puss on the hind quarters. I sprung forward but not fast enough to keep its jagged teeth from tearing into pussycat's silky flank. YOWL! cried Petronella as I attacked the fox from behind and dug my claws into its mangy back. It whipped round and caught me by the hock, sinking its teeth through layers of skin and muscle to my bone.

GRRR-OWWW! I screeched to the treetops while flailing at its head with outstretched claws. It let go my leg to concentrate upon my gut and I did not know if those gleaming teeth would rip me apart. Until suddenly, on the outskirts of my pain I heard a banging door and the roar of a stunted lion. For Dog had heard the melee and was flying down the hill growling from Its bowels with the menace of all its ancestors. My would-be assassin looked up to see the Chow set upon it with the rage of a she-bear fighting for her young.

It was a horrific scuffle. Fox and Dog grappling in deadly battle -- one for its offspring, the other for its ground. Petronella dragged herself under a bush, the cub was stumbling to get up from under the conifer while I lay wounded and bleeding near the fence.

From out of nowhere She appeared at the top of the garden. With broom in hand, screaming, "Tamba!" Her shriek startled both combatants but the fox recovered first to sink its teeth into Dog's soft white belly unprotected by much fur. Dog squealed with pain as blood spurted forth and so loud and tortured was the Chow's cry that with Her shouting, the vixen backed off and left her cub.

Then all was quiet in the garden except for the muted cries of a broken little fox, the injured silence of two cats and a softly whimpering dog in the presence of one dead squirrel as She fled into the house.

Monday, 26th April: *A Shakespearean tragedy*

I am feeling weak and horribly sore from the cut and thrust of battle. Dog is still in hospital. Reading in between the lines of all Her conversations since our attempted murders by the rampaging vixen, I infer She did not subtly encourage the vet to make a house call but forcefully demanded his presence given "the one already dead body and many others who will surely die if someone doesn't get over here RIGHT BLOODY NOW!"

Our vet, who brought an assistant along with half a dozen portable kennels with him, said to his colleague out of Her earshot but not mine that the scene in our garden reminded him of "the last act of a Shakespeare play with lots of corpses lying around the stage." The assistant chuckled, which I deemed a most callous response in the grass and shrub of bloodshed.

Silver Puss was "more scared than badly hurt although she looked a holy mess," they said after crawling into the bushes to retrieve and jab her for the pain. "The fox cub must have gone walkabout," speculated the vet. "Possibly fell off the fence and broke its leg." The Stinking Squirrel did not die as I'd imagined. "Not a mark on him," said the vet. "May have misjudged the distance before a jump and plummeted to his death." As for me, the vet just shook his head, "Well, Mr Cat, you've certainly been through the wars this year. But you'll live to pounce again." After jabbing me and looking me over, he told Her my hock had taken "a serious mauling" but that the bone was "still intact."

Dog was their biggest worry as she was "bleeding profusely" but with the same astuteness I'd observed when first I clawed her lip, the Chow did not rail against her plight, simply waited patiently for men to choose her course. "Don't worry," the vet said to Her. "She's young and strong and it's not nearly as bad as it looks."

I was able to come home later in the day after they'd pulled and prodded me and sewed me up. My hock resembles a chicken leg shaved to the thigh but at least it's all clean and tidy and I can drag it behind me. Isn't it strange how events repeat themselves, except this time it wasn't me who fell but the Stinking Squirrel.

Tuesday, 27th April: *The experience of surviving*

Dog came home this morning. I could tell the Chow was struggling to cope with her injuries by the way she slowly and stiffly padded through the door. Her tummy has been shaved, it's got stitches in it and the vet's making Dog wear a bandage around her middle so she doesn't scratch them out. The Chow is exceptionally quiet and subdued and in a lot of pain, I think, although the vet says Dog's wounds "are not especially deep" and she'll be "right as rain" within a few weeks. But I note Dog did not eat a thing today. Thus I am concerned about her state.

I suppose the difference is – I've seen so much more of life than she, that while Sunday's carnage was awful, it was for me only a confluence of unfortunate circumstances, all of which I've seen before. Whereas despite her instinctive knowing, Dog does not yet have the experience of surviving many fights or falls. So albeit injured, when I am hungry, I will eat and when I'm thirsty, I will drink. Therefore, tonight when Dog settles upon her carpet remnant, I shall rest on the edge of the bed nearest to where doggy lies to guard our Tamba while she sleeps.

Thursday, 29th April: *A loyal and fearsome ally*

I am pleased to note, Dog has perked up considerably since coming out of hospital. We both went back to the vet today for a check and he is satisfied we're making "excellent progress" although we'll be kept on "pain killers" for a few more days. I am once again a three-legged cat. Which is extremely irritating as visits to Petronella will be severely curtailed for some weeks to come. However, I console myself with the knowledge that Silver Puss needs time to recover and I must be grateful that she's all right. Fender-Bender said as much when she popped in this evening to see how Dog and I are doing.

Over glasses of wine in the lounge, She and our neighbour tried to piece together "the Shakespearean tragedy of the weekend maulings," as the vet insists on calling the incident when it's not being labelled by others as "a cautionary tale about a mother's instincts to defend an injured child." So far they've all failed to recognise Dog's courage and bravery in rushing forward to rescue

274

me from more serious injury. I however do appreciate the enormity of what Tamba has done and will not forget her act. Indeed, it strikes me that with proper training, a Chow could be a most loyal and fearsome ally to A. S. Cat.

Friday, 30th April: *Light at the end of the tunnel*

Today is Her birthday. "Nothing significant" She says to anyone who asks. When Her mother called, She said she was taking the day off to "take care of the pets."

In the early afternoon an enormous bouquet of flowers arrived. I sat crookedly in the hallway and watched Her intercept them. *Another grandiose gesture of unfulfilled promise from the Hound,* I asked with my tail twitching? She carried them into the kitchen. I limped in after Her. As She ripped open their card, I started rubbing against Her ankles. She leaned down to pick me up very gently and set me down on the counter.

"Yes, Sooty, two dozen red roses from 'the time waster,' " She said matter of factly. She paused and to my delight added, "And you know what? Frankly, I don't give a damn!"   Taking a deep breath, She squared her shoulders and tore at the wrapping. "To make a new beginning, Puss, I shall make a definitive end!" I purred approval as with deft precision She mercilessly beheaded and scissored every flower into the bin.

For dinner She made us "special treats": ham and cheese bits for me and sausages for Dog. Then She ordered herself a take-away tandoori chicken from her favourite Indian restaurant. The kitchen soon smelled of cumin, cloves and ginger root. Afterwards we all went into the lounge. Even though it's spring, it was chilly enough for a fire. She poured herself a bulbous glass of something orange-scented and lifted me onto the sofa beside her where She started stroking me and staring into the flames. Dog lay quietly at our feet and I cast my mind back over the events of Her past year.

If I'm honest, before Dog arrived I had feared She was heading for the rack and ruin of being a too hard business woman. Now I am more optimistic about Her future. It's a shame She wasn't ready to meet the Precocious Brat. She claims *she* sent him packing but She lies in my estimation. For I believe he left of his own volition, not because he's squirrelous but because he has cat's wisdom. More than likely he told her not to blame him for her discomfort but look to self. I only hope -- one day The Brat will knock upon her door again with a large bouquet of white roses and find Her greatly changed.

In the meantime I now see -- Dog and I could work together to take Her more firmly under our wing. For there *is* light at the end of Her rat tunnel when all is said and done. As for Tamba, I confess – I've grown accustomed to her furry face if not her hidden smile.

THE END

(And mice chase cats… don't they!)

The character of A. S. Cat is based on a real black-and-white neutered tom called Sooty who was bought for £5 by D. H. Carter in 1988 from an animal shelter in Newcastle upon Tyne

in northern England. A dog warden found Sooty wandering along the streets of a suburb. With a glossy coat, he looked quite well fed and was very friendly. No one came forward to claim the sleek young tom so he was put up for adoption. While Sooty's owner thought him to be the "bee's knees," Puss was in reality no more than a lovely example of the quite common piebald or "tuxedo" cat, a mainly black moggy with solid patches of white fur. In Sooty's case these covered his paws, bib, nose and chin and with his white undercoat, he appeared "a cut above the rest."

Sooty's behaviour was "exemplary." He was generally quiet and reserved except at mealtimes when the "meows" became loud and insistent. And Sooty was very affectionate, and happy to set up house in anyone's lap.

In early 2004 Sooty's vet diagnosed him as diabetic. Although he needed insulin injections twice a day, Sooty never complained, taking every jab in his stride during morning and evening meals.

Throughout his long life Sooty was a contented little chap whom everyone loved, including his one-time nemesis, an exceptionally curious Chow Chow called Tamba.

ALL ABOUT CATS

General Overview

Cats are remarkable household pets whose natures are shrouded in mystery and fascination. Graceful, enigmatic and extraordinarily independent, they are said to have powers of extrasensory perception bordering on supernatural.

For centuries cats have been immortalised in art, literature, music and myriad other forms of human self-expression. The famed American poet T. S. Eliot raised their profile during the first half of the 20th century with his delightful *Old Possum's Book of Practical Cats* while Britain's Andrew Lloyd-Webber translated Eliot's verse almost 50 years later into the long-running *Cats* musical.

According to historians, cats have lived amongst us for the past 5,000 years although they've been in existence an estimated 40 million. Today's big cats of the wild, lions and tigers, descended from early weasel-like creatures called *miacids* which later developed into the European wild cat, African wild cat and Asiatic desert cat. The domestic cat is believed to have descended from the African strain because of its tabby markings.

Facts about Cats

Description: hunting carnivores and members of the *Felidea* family, appearing in diverse shapes and sizes with fur of varying colours and textures, strong predatory instincts, acute hearing and excellent vision in dim light.

Breeds: 36 currently recognised, of which the Siamese is most popular with most common house pet being non-pedigree black-and-white moggy.

Total number worldwide: estimated at 400 million, including 9 million in the UK alone, in the year 2000.

278

Lifespan: 10-15 years on average although 40 years reported.

Character: intelligent, agile, friendly and affectionate albeit very self-contained in nature.

Behaviour: possessed of a strong hunting instinct; acts independent; communicates by sound, the way it holds itself and through movements of its ears and tail

Potted history

- First domesticated in 3,500 B.C. by the Ancient Egyptians after which became revered as hunters and even worshipped (e.g. the god Bast)
- Appeared in Europe and the Middle East around 1,000 B.C. with traders. Were used to protect food stores from vermin.
- Reached Japan by 999 A.D. where emerged in their art
- During the Black Death in the 1300s, helped kill rats which carried disease-spreading fleas causing bubonic plague.
- Became associated with witchcraft during the Middle Ages during which thousands were killed; black cats in particular were thought by some to be the devil incarnate.
- Brought to America in the 1600s and 1700s.
- By the 1800s regained popularity as 'mousers' and pets

Even more amazing...

- Domestic cats can run about 30 mph.
- A cat's sense of smell is calculated to be 14 times stronger than a human's.
- Cats have about 100 different vocalisation sounds.
- A cat can jump 5 times higher than it is tall.
- Cats are supersensitive: the cat may detect variations in electromagnetic fields, air pressure and other atmospheric conditions which humans are incapable of perceiving.

Information sources: www.catsinfo.com, www.purr-n-fur.org.uk

The Next Pets Diary: Join Our Waiting List

The next pets diary in development is Chow dog Tamba's entitled *A Very Tall Dog Story* (unless of course she changes it!). Tamba, who's disdainfully called "Dog" by cat Sooty in *Life in the Cat's Lane*, tells her own story about life, love and the pursuit of happiness in a cat-run household.

To place your name on our waiting list as a prospective purchaser, visit our website at **www.mspec.co.uk** and leave us a message with all your contact details. Alternatively, complete the form below. Then detach it and post it to us at: **Mspec.co.uk, P.O Box 936, Camberley GU15 9EG**. You will be under no obligation to purchase the book but sending us your details will enable us to let you know when it becomes available.

- -

Your name:

First name _____

Last name _____

Mailing address:

House/flat number _____

Street number   _____

Town/city   _____

State/county   _____

Country   _____

Postal code   _____

Contact details:

Email _____ Tel: _____

CAT'S LANE LITERARY QUIZ

Feline linguistics experts note that Sooty, an English moggy of undisputed intellect, lapses into language reminiscent of Shakespeare although the cat has never been observed to read any. Yet, his diary is peppered with words and phrases to make The Bard proud. Some of that verbiage has already been identified. More is being uncovered daily. Can YOU name the plays which may have influenced the cat's mutterings?

Among other things Sooty says in his diary:

1. PRRR MAXIMUS! _They_ stumble who run fast at me -- DOG has been sound blasted into submission by "newspaper intimidation."

2. As I lie on the edge of sleep in my igloo bed, I ask myself – how can I expose such falsehood thriving behind closed doors?

3. And thus was I forced into the vilest of acts, to lose my honour and myself in having to behave like a dog -- and indiscreetly pee.

4. DOG is no dimwit, only a corrupt manipulator of the truth that friendly eyes never see faults.

5. Seconds later our noses touched. And I could only marvel at how love's gentle spring always fresh remains.

Do tell the publisher if you find any others. Thank you.

Some Shakespeare Play Titles (for quick reference):
Anthony & Cleopatra, Hamlet, Henry VIII, Julius Caesar, Macbeth, Much Ado, Othello, Richard III, Romeo & Juliet, Venus & Adonis

The Editor

D. H. Carter, born in the USA, has lived in the UK for more than 20 years after working in North America, Mexico and Spain. The Editor is a passionate lover of animals, most especially cats and dogs.

The Illustrator

C. J. Allen enjoys landscape painting with watercolours and has only recently ventured into creating cartoon illustrations. Her paintings have been exhibited in both the South of England and New York City. Part of her family is a Burmese cat called Jaspar with "more than enough to say for himself!"